The Abingdon Religious Education Texts
David G. Downey, General Editor
DAILY VACATION CHURCH SCHOOL SERIES
GEORGE HERBERT BETTS, Editor

Knights of Service

(For Children of 9-11 years)

BY

EMERSON O. BRADSHAW

Secretary, Commission on Religious Education
The Chicago Church Federation

Prepared in Cooperation with the International Association
of Daily Vacation Bible Schools

THE ABINGDON PRESS
NEW YORK   CINCINNATI

Printed in the United States of America

First Edition Printed June, 1923
Reprinted July, 1924, March, 1926

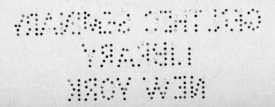

CONTENTS

CONTENTS

PART II.—CHARACTER STORIES

FOREWORD

THE teacher who has learned the art of telling effectively a good story is sure of an appreciative hearing from children. Story-borne truth is peculiarly effective with childhood, for it fires the imagination and kindles interest while at the same time making the lesson so concrete that its meaning cannot be escaped. Furthermore, the teacher who has mastered the art of story-telling has learned the mind and heart of the child, for childhood thinks and feels in terms of the picturesque and the real as set forth in good stories.

Many types of teaching are suited to the junior classroom, but none take precedence over the story method. The story may well be made the basis of other forms of instruction, as when it supplies the material for dramatization, or opens up a line of discussion, or suggests problems and projects to be investigated and followed out.

Two classes of stories are presented in this volume: A group of Bible stories centered about the great interests and fundamental virtues which are suitable for junior children; and another group intended to reinforce the lessons presented through these Bible stories, but from a somewhat different point of view. The two series, therefore, supplement each other, though either can, of course, be used separately.

This book was prepared especially to accompany *Knights of Service: Program Guide* (of this same Series), by Marion O. Hawthorne, but it is hoped that it will serve equally well in any other phase of the church school or in the home where stories are told to children. The volume is definitely planned *as a textbook for the pupils themselves in vacation church-school classes.* GEORGE H. BETTS.

5

PART I. BIBLE STORIES

I

JESUS OUR HEROIC MASTER

JERUSALEM, the Holy City, was buzzing with excitement. In a very few days the Feast of the Passover would be celebrated. Already the crowds from the outlying districts were pouring into the city. Men, women, and children filled the streets, and everywhere there was hustle and confusion.

But never before had there been quite as much excitement. On every hand, in the market place, on the streets, in the porches of the Temple, everyone was talking about the same thing. Even the little children, busy at their play, called merrily to one another the wonderful news.

"The King is coming! The Messiah for whom we have waited so many years is drawing nigh! It is Jesus of Nazareth who shall establish the Kingdom of the Jews upon the earth!" Like wildfire the news spread, and it seemed that every arrival in the city had some new story to tell of the power and wonderful deeds of Jesus.

"He hath cured Peter's wife's mother, who lay ill of a fever," one told a group of interested listeners. "Jairus' daughter lay dead and he hath brought her back to life again!" another tale was told. "With stories that he calls parables he hath taught us many things about the kingdom of God," said yet another. There came also one from Bethany, telling what had happened to Lazarus: "Lo! he was dead and they had placed him in the tomb," thrillingly he told the story, "and when the Master came and found them weeping he entered the tomb, and when he came out, lo! Lazarus, full of health and life, was with him!"

On the Sabbath afternoon (which is our Saturday) the news reached Jerusalem that on the morrow the King would enter the city. "I can hardly wait to see the King!" children said to one another, and they wished the hours would pass more quickly.

"Surely he will come riding upon a gallant war horse, and leading an army with banners and trumpets! He will strike down at a word those who refuse to honor him!" many of the people thought, and they could hardly wait for his appearance.

The dawn came with a burst of gold and rose color the first day of the week, and it looked as though the very skies were thrilling with anticipation. Everyone in the city was stirring early, for they knew not at what hour the King would come. It seemed to them that they had been waiting for hours, when there came running through a gate nearest the little village of Bethphage a youth, panting with his run, and bursting with excitement

"Ho! Everyone!" he shouted, "the King cometh! He has left Bethphage riding upon a colt. Soon he will be here!" And away he darted to spread his good news. Finally, standing in the market place, a group of men pressed tightly around him, he told them how two disciples of Jesus had come into Bethphage, and had unloosed a colt that stood tied outside a house there. "And when the owner questioned the two men they said, 'The Lord hath need of him!'" Wonder clouded the faces of his listeners. Some of them looked disappointed. Was the King coming, riding upon a colt? Where was the fiery war horse they had felt sure he would ride? Where were the victorious armies they had expected? Perhaps he wasn't the King at all!

Then a man, standing in the crowd, turned and spoke reverently: "Even so hath the prophet spoken, 'Behold thy king cometh to thee; he is just, and having salvation; lowly, and riding upon a colt!'" And a shout of exaltation echoed through the market place. He was to be their King after all!

Toward the gate through which the King must come the crowds hastened. As they went they cut palm branches and gathered flowers. Some of the children and youths who could run swiftly hastened outside the city walls, where crocuses, tulips, and geraniums were blooming in great quantities. Bringing whole handfuls of the fragrant blossoms, they hurried back to the city. Soon the edges of the roads were lined with people. Old men and women were there, with faces shining with joy; mothers had brought tiny babies, and held them tenderly in their arms, crooning, "To-day shalt thou see thy King, my little one!"

Suddenly, a shout, "Hosanna!" rent the air. It was quickly taken up by the multitude of throats, until it seemed that the whole world was filled with the shout, "Hosanna!"

And then they saw him coming! His body swayed easily with the motion of the beast, his white robes moved gently in the breeze, and his splendid head was thrown back as he gazed out upon the crowd. "Hosanna! Hosanna!" they cried, and the little children along the way strewed flowers in his path. Men threw down their garments and the graceful palm branches, until the stones were covered with a thick covering into which the hoofs of the colt sank without a jar.

"Hosanna to the Son of David! Hail! King of the Jews!" the cry resounded all along the way. "Hail! Jesus of Nazareth, King of the Jews!" And so the Christ rode into the Holy City of Jerusalem on that Palm Sunday, nearly two thousand years ago.

II

SAMSON, A MAN OF STRENGTH

A YOUNG boy was playing outside one of the tents of the Israelites. Sitting near by, where she could be sure that he came to no harm, was his mother.

"How strong he is!" she said to herself. "Such a beautiful child will some day perform wondrous deeds. Perhaps he may even deliver our people from our enemies the Philistines!"

That night she talked with her husband, Manoah, about their child. "Surely," she told him, "our son hath been sent to do a great work." And she and Manoah dreamed of the day when perhaps Samson, their only son, might regain the freedom of the Israelites.

From babyhood Samson had been an unusually strong child. People talked about him with wonder as they watched how he grew sturdier with every day. "Oh, that my little Caleb were like Samson!" one mother wished, as she looked at her own frail little son. "I must ask Manoah's wife to help me, so that my son, too, may grow strong." Even Samson's father and mother marveled at the strength of the child, and in every way they did all in their power to increase the child's health and make him even stronger.

"Ask Samson to get it for you." One of the boys had thrown the scarf which he wore about his head high into a tall tree, and it had lodged among the

branches. "Our Samson can swim the stream,"
boasted the Israelite boys to the Philistine youths,
as they stood watching the swift current of a tur-
bulent brook, swollen with mountain snows. "Samson can run as fast as an eagle's flight!" bragged
his companions. Nor was their joy empty, for
so carefully had Samson been trained and so
strong was his body that he had never failed in
any feat which he had attempted, even in the face
of danger.

Samson's life had been set apart for God by his
parents. "Our son," said Manoah to his wife, after
Samson was become a man, "must be nearly ready
to do the work for which God has called him, and
for which we have so carefully prepared him."

"Perhaps," his wife answered, "there is some test
which he must meet before God will find him ready.
Let us pray that whatever happens his strength and
his courage will never leave him."

Finally the day of testing came, when Samson
had gone with his father and mother on a journey
to Timnah. In his great strength, and because of his
eagerness to reach the city, Samson had far out-
distanced his mother and father. He had at last
reached the vineyards of Timnah and was happy to
think that his journey was almost over.

Suddenly a deep-throated roar tore the air! Again
it sounded, and yet again! For a moment Samson's
heart stopped beating. He had heard tales of the
fierce lions that sometimes came almost into the
very city.

Only for a second did Samson's courage waver,
then he squared his shoulders and braced his legs
securely. He had no weapon, and there was no one

near who could help him. It must be a bare-handed
fight against the savage beast!

There was a crackling of leaves and twigs, another
roar, and then, bounding swiftly toward him, its
breath coming in short gusts of anger, was the fierce
animal.

Samson took a deep breath. Swift and sure were
his motions. There was a howl of pain from the
beast, and then, with ease, he tossed the torn form
of the lion into the bushes!

The lad, whom his parents had so long been
training, had met his first mighty test of strength;
his strong muscles had not failed him nor had his
courage been lacking in the time of great need.

It was some time later that he told his parents of
the fight and his victory. "Surely his time has come,"
they said, with gladness to each other. "Samson,
our beloved son, is ready to start his fight against
the enemies of our people."

III

DAVID AND HIS COUNTRY

THE Philistine army and the army of Israel had come together in a great battle. The Bible tells us that the Philistines were standing on the hill on one side, and the Israelites were standing on the hill on the other side, with the valley between.

The place was not far from Bethlehem, where lived a man named Jesse, three of whose sons were fighting with Saul, commander of the army of Israel. Every few days Jesse sent his youngest son David to carry a basket of food to his soldier brothers.

One day while David was at the camp of the Israelites he saw a great soldier giant come down the hill from the Philistines and stop in the valley below where Saul's army was encamped. His name was Goliath, and he was the champion soldier of the Philistines. He was very large and very strong. He wore a costly uniform of shining brass, and carried a great spear with an iron head.

The breastplate which the giant fighter wore weighed one hundred and fifty pounds. He also had bronze greaves upon his leg, and a bronze back plate between his shoulders. The shaft of his spear was like a weaver's beam, and the head of his iron spear weighed about twenty pounds; and his shield-bearer went before him.

Every day for forty days this giant had come down into the valley between the armies. Every

16

day he had thrown out the challenge, "Give me a man that we may fight together."

Saul looked among his soldiers for a man, but in vain. He offered rich rewards to the one who would go out and conquer Goliath. But not one of the soldiers of Israel would offer to fight the giant. They were all afraid of his great size, his fierce look, and his mighty spear. "All of the men of Israel, when they saw the man, fled from him, and were sore afraid." Even David's three brothers were afraid like the rest. But David, when he saw Goliath come down into the valley and heard him roar out his challenge, was not afraid. He said to his brothers, "I will go to King Saul and ask his permission to fight the giant."

His brothers scorned him and laughed at him, and said, "Why have you come down? And with whom have you left those few sheep in the wilderness? We know the pride and the naughtiness of your heart, for you have come down to see the battle. Will you now think to fight this mighty man of the Philistines!"

But David paid no heed to their slighting words. He was loyal to his country and he loved and worshiped Jehovah the God of Israel. He believed that Jehovah wanted him to serve his country, and that with God's help he could conquer the giant enemy. So David came to King Saul and said, "I will go out and fight this Philistine."

The king was astonished, and said, "You are not able to go and fight against this Philistine, for you are only a youth and he has been a warrior from his youth."

David, nothing daunted, replied to the king,

"Your servant kept his father's sheep, and whenever a lion or bear came and took a lamb out of the flock, I would go out after him and kill him and rescue it from his mouth. If he attacked me I would seize him by the throat and kill him with a blow. Your servant hath killed both lion and bear."

"Now this heathen Philistine," he said, "shall be like one of them, for he has taunted the armies of the living God. Jehovah, who delivered me from the paw of the lion and the paw of the bear, will deliver me from the hand of this Philistine."

Then Saul said to David, "Go, and may Jehovah be with you."

So David, the young shepherd lad, prepared to meet the mighty Goliath in battle. King Saul offered David his own armor, but David put it aside; for he had his own plans. Bravely he left the presence of Saul and started down the hill toward the haughty giant. The eyes of all the soldiers were turned toward David. His danger was great, but his heart was strong and his hand steady. Instead of a spear he carried with him his sling, with which he had so often defended his father's sheep.

As he crossed the little brook on his way to meet Goliath, he picked up five smooth round stones from the bed of the brook. Calmly he put them in his shepherd's bag.

Nearer and nearer he came to the waiting enemy, who loudly mocked at him. A deep silence fell on both sides. Each army watched every move that David made. The fate of Israel was in his hands. The safety of his country depended upon him.

David was not afraid. He trusted Jehovah to give him strength for the battle. When the giant taunted him with being but a boy, he answered, "I come to thee in the name of Jehovah of Hosts, the God of the armies of Israel. This day will Jehovah deliver thee into my hands."

When David had come quite near to Goliath, the Philistine took his great sword and started toward him. Still David was not afraid. He still believed he would win in the name of Jehovah.

Just at the right moment David carefully drew from his shepherd's bag one of the round stones and put it in his sling. He raised the sling, took aim and shot the stone with all his might. It hit the giant fairly and sank deep into his forehead. Down he fell upon his face to the ground. David had won the day!

When the Philistines saw their great leader go down before the slender boy of Israel they turned and fled. The whole army took to its heels. Saul's army raised the battle cry and pursued the retreating Philistines. The Israelites won a great battle that day. Their homes were again made safe and their women and children set free from the hands of the Philistines.

All Israel honored David, the young shepherd, who had trusted Jehovah to help him save his country. Israel now had peace, and David was in great favor with all the people.

IV

RUTH THE FAITHFUL

On a lonely road between Moab and Bethlehem, three women, Naomi, Ruth, and Orpah, stood weeping. The gray hair and drooping figure of Naomi showed that she was growing old. Ruth and Orpah were young and beautiful. Naomi's home was in Bethlehem; Ruth and Orpah lived in the land of Moab. They were sad because they were about to part, perhaps never to meet again. This is their story:

Many years before, the crops had failed at Bethlehem and there had been famine in the land. At that time Naomi, with her husband and her two sons, had left their Bethlehem home and moved to the land of Moab, where the food was plentiful. They prospered while they were living in Moab, and one of Naomi's sons had married Ruth and the other had married Orpah.

Then a great sorrow came to them. Elimelech, Naomi's husband, fell sick and died. After that, Naomi made her home with her two sons and their wives, Ruth and Orpah, who did everything they could to make her comfortable and happy.

But, sad to relate, after some years had passed, both of the sons sickened and died. So Naomi, Ruth, and Orpah were left alone in the land of Moab. Ruth and Orpah loved Naomi as if she had been their own mother; but Naomi, with her husband and sons gone, became homesick to see her old friends in Bethlehem and decided to return there. It was a long walk of many miles from Moab to Bethlehem. Naomi had planned to make the trip all alone, for she would not think of taking Ruth and Orpah away from their friends and relatives.

When Naomi started on her journey, Ruth and Orpah, sorrowing, went part way with her. They had walked some distance, and the time had now come for them to turn back; and it made them all very sad, for they loved each other dearly. So there they stood weeping as they were saying good-bye.

Turning to her two daughters, Naomi said to them, "Go, return each of you to her mother's house; and the Lord deal kindly with you, as ye have dealt with me."

Ruth and Orpah answered, "Nay, you shall not go alone, we will go with thee to thy people."

Naomi again urged them to return to their own kindred. Orpah was convinced; she kissed her and turned back. But Ruth clung to Naomi and said:

"Entreat me not to leave thee; for whither thou goest I will go, and where thou lodgest I will lodge. Thy people shall be my people, and thy God my God."

So Ruth left her home and her kindred and her friends to go with Naomi, because she loved her. They went on together until they reached Bethlehem, Naomi's old home. It was midsummer when they arrived and they found the farmers busy with their sickles, harvesting the fields of wheat and barley.

Naomi and Ruth were very poor and had no money with which to buy food. Now it was the custom in that country for the reapers to allow the poor to follow after them, gleaning the fallen grain and taking it for food. Ruth therefore went out in the barley fields to glean, as did the other maidens.

The field in which she found herself belonged to Boaz, a kinsman of Naomi's. When Boaz saw Ruth busily gleaning after the reapers, he asked, "Whose maiden is this?" They answered him that she was Ruth, of Moab, who had come to Bethlehem with Naomi.

Then Boaz spoke kindly to Ruth and told her that she was welcome to glean in his fields, and that she was to have water from the pitchers the men had drawn from the well. When lunch time came he asked her to eat with them. So Ruth gleaned in the fields of Boaz until the end of the harvest, and found food for herself and Naomi.

Boaz had not failed to notice the beautiful Ruth as she gleaned so faithfully day after day, and he had also learned of her kindness to aged Naomi. He came to love her, and asked her to be his wife. Soon they were married and lived happily for many years in Bethlehem.

V

JOSEPH AND HIS BROTHERS

"FOR whom are you looking?" asked a stranger, who found the lad Joseph wandering in the field as if he were lost.

"I am looking for my brothers," said Joseph. "There are ten of them. They are shepherds, and they came out here to tend my father's sheep. Can you tell me where I may find them?"

"Two days ago," answered the man, "they were here tending their sheep in this very field. I heard one of them say, 'Let us take our sheep to Dothan.' So if you will go on to that place, no doubt you will find them there." So Joseph thanked the man kindly and set out at once for Dothan.

Now Joseph's father's name was Jacob, and his home was in Hebron. Jacob had sent his sons with the flocks of sheep to find better fields for pasture. It was forty or fifty miles from their home, so they had to camp out in the fields with their sheep during the summer.

The sons had now been away from home a long time and Jacob was anxious to know how they were prospering, and whether the flocks were safe. So he sent Joseph out to find his brothers and to bring back a report about them and the sheep.

"Here comes the dreamer," said the brothers, when they saw Joseph coming in the distance. The reason they called him a dreamer was because long

before they came to Dothan with the flocks Joseph
told them about two dreams he had had.

It had been like this: One morning when Joseph
got up he said to his brothers: "I had a wonderful
dream last night, which I want to tell you about.
In my dream it was harvest time and we were
binding sheaves in the field. There were twelve of
us and we each had a sheaf of wheat. Then suddenly
the twelve sheaves stood up. My sheaf remained
still, and behold your eleven sheaves came before
my sheaf and bowed to the ground before it, as if it
were king of all the sheaves."

Now people believed in dreams in those days, and
Joseph's dream made the brethren very envious.
They said, "Do you think that some day you will
become a king and will rule over us, your brothers?"

On another morning Joseph told his brothers yet
another dream which he had dreamed. "In this
dream," he said, "it seemed as if the sun and the
moon and eleven stars came where I was, and bowed
very low, as if to show me great respect and great
reverence."

His father also heard him tell about this dream.
"What is this dream that thou hast dreamed?" said
Jacob. "Shall I and thy mother and thy brethren
indeed come to bow down ourselves before thee
to the earth?" But Joseph made no answer. The
brothers were still more envious of him after the
second dream; but the father pondered over the
matter, wondering what it could mean.

So when the brothers saw Joseph coming to where
they were at Dothan they remembered the dreams,
which seemed to say that Joseph would some day
rule over them like a king.

When Joseph had come nearer they looked at him more closely, and behold he had on the long beautiful coat with flowing sleeves and of many colors. His father had given him this wonderful coat, so fine that it was such as princes wore. To them it seemed as if a young prince were coming to their camp.

The dreams and the coat were too much for the shepherd brothers. So they began to plot how they might be rid of Joseph, even before he had come to where they were. "Come let us kill him and throw him into one of the pits," they said, "and then we will see what becomes of his dreams. We will tell our father that a fierce beast has devoured him."

But Reuben said, "Do not take his life, but let us put him in one of these deepest pits which are used to hold water in the rainy season. The pits are dry now, but they are so deep that he could never get out."

Reuben made this plan thinking that he would slip around to the pit when his brothers were not looking and help Joseph out and send him home to his father.

By this time Joseph had reached their camp. Without even speaking to him they laid hold of him and stripped off his long, princely coat. Then they dragged him to one of the deepest pits and put him in.

After that they went back to their camp and began to eat their dinner. They did not so much as think of throwing a piece of bread to Joseph, who must have been hungry from his long journey.

While the brothers were eating, they looked up and saw coming in the distance a caravan of camels. The camels were carrying heavy packs filled with spices and other precious things. They were on their way to the markets of Egypt.

Then Judah, one of the brothers, said, "It would be wrong for us to take the life of Joseph, for he is our brother. Come, let us sell him to the camel drivers."

When the camel drivers came up the brothers said, "We have a young man here whom we would like to sell to you for a slave"; and they went to the pit and drew Joseph up. The bargain was soon made, for the camel drivers agreed to give them twelve dollars for Joseph.

Now, the brothers thought, "This is the last of Joseph, the dreamer and prince, who would rule over us."

When the caravan had gone on, these wicked brothers killed a goat, took the blood, smeared it over Joseph's coat of many colors and carried it home to their father Jacob.

They said to their father, "We found this coat in the field all covered with blood like this. Is it not Joseph's coat?"

The aged father was overcome with grief. He cried out, "It is indeed my son's coat, which I gave to him. Joseph, my beloved son, has been torn to pieces. A wild beast has devoured him!"

Jacob mourned for his son Joseph for many days. So great was his grief that the brothers thought he would surely die. They tried to comfort him, but he said, "This sorrow is so great that I shall go down to my grave mourning for my son."

VI

JOSEPH RETURNS GOOD FOR EVIL

MANY years had passed since his wicked brothers had sold Joseph down into Egypt as a slave. Jacob, the father, had never ceased to grieve over his lost son. To-day he sat with bowed head, his hands clasped upon his staff, his heart filled with sorrow and perplexity. A famine had come upon the land, the crops had failed, and soon there would be no food either for those of his household or for the animals. Money he had in plenty, but money was of no use when there was no food to buy.

Jacob's sons gathered about him; but their faces also were sad and their hearts heavy, for their barns were empty and their families wanted for food. They were sorrowful to see their father troubled in his old age, but could do nought to help him.

At last they ventured to say to Jacob: "We have been told that there is grain to spare in the land of Egypt. We have been told that the king of that land has put a governor in charge of his stores of grain. We will take much money with us and perhaps he will sell us enough to keep us alive."

So Jacob gave his sons his blessing, and they took their empty sacks on their animals and journeyed down into Egypt. Only the younger brother, Benjamin, stayed at home with his father.

Now Benjamin was the apple of his father's eye. Ever since Joseph had disappeared, Jacob had watched over Benjamin and loved him very ten-

derly. Perhaps the other brothers were sorry by
this time for the way they had treated Joseph and
for their father's sorrow over him. Indeed, they
did not even ask for Benjamin to go with them, but
left him to comfort their father in their absence.

When Jacob's ten sons had come into Egypt they
found that grain was being sold from the king's
storehouse under the direction of the governor, who
was an officer of the king's own household. Other
buyers who had come before them had their sacks
filled with grain and went on their way. When the
ten brothers appeared before the head officer, he
saw that they were strangers from another land,
and asked of them, "Whence come you?"

They answered, "We come from the land of
Canaan to buy grain for food, for there is a famine
in that land, and those of our household are ready
to die of want."

But the governor of the king's storehouses answered, "How do I know that you are not spies,
come down to spy upon our land? I will not sell
you grain unless you can prove who you are."

Strongly did the brothers protest: "We are no
spies. We are all brothers, the sons of one father,
and we are good men and true, who have come
down into Egypt to buy grain, because there is a
famine in the land of Canaan, where we live."

Still the governor was not convinced. He said,
"You must prove to me that what you say is true."

Then the brothers began to tell the story of their
family. They said, "There are twelve brothers of
us; but one of our brothers is dead, and the youngest
one is now at home with our father, who is growing
old."

Then said the governor: "If you would have me believe that this is true, you must bring your youngest brother here, that I may see him. One of you must go and get him, and the other nine must remain here under guard."

Upon this command the ten brothers were in deep despair. They knew that their father would not give his consent to have Benjamin come down into Egypt. They feared that this cruel governor might not allow them to go home, and that if he did he would send them away empty, as they came.

For three days the governor kept all the brothers prisoners under guard. Then he sent for them to come before him. "I have decided," he said, "to sell you the grain, and allow nine of you to go home with it. But one of you must remain here as hostage until the rest return with this youngest brother, of whom you have told me, and let it be known to you that you can have no more grain, nor will I ever allow you again to come into my presence unless you bring this boy back with you."

So Simeon agreed to stay as a hostage in the governor's house, while the nine brothers returned to the land of Canaan with the grain that was to keep their father and their households from starving.

The sacks were filled with grain, the money paid, and the sacks loaded on the animals. In the meantime, however, the governor had given a secret order that the money should be put back into the top of each of the sacks of grain.

While they were on their journey home the brothers opened their sacks to take out grain for food, and there they found the money which they had paid for the grain. They were filled with astonishment and fear, not knowing why this strange thing should be done. Nor when they had told their father about the money, could he explain it any more than they.

When they had told their father of the command of the governor to bring Benjamin to him, Jacob said: "I will never let Benjamin leave me to go down into Egypt. Behold, did I not send my son Joseph on an errand away from home and he never returned; and now shall I likewise lose Benjamin?"

But, after a time the grain which the brothers had brought from Egypt had all been eaten, and there was no food to be had in the land. The brothers came before their father and said: "Not only Benjamin, but all of us must die, for we have no grain. The governor said we should not even look upon his face again except we bring Benjamin with us." Judah, one of the brothers, stood forth and said:

"I will be surety for him; of my hand shalt thou require him: if I bring him not to thee, and set him before thee, then let me bear the blame forever: for except we had lingered, surely we had now returned a second time."

So Jacob gave his consent for Benjamin to return with his brothers down into Egypt. They took many rich presents with them, hoping to win the favor of the governor and to prove that they had not meant to carry away the money which they had paid for the grain on their first trip.

Now, when the governor heard that the brothers were at the gate asking again to buy grain, he sent an order to his chief cook, saying, "Make to-day a great feast, for I shall have as guests these men from Canaan, who will dine with me."

The brothers came before the governor with great fear, remembering how the money had been found in their sacks; but he said to them, "Fear not!" and he had their brother, Simeon, who had been held as hostage, brought out to see them, and they found him sound and well.

When they were gathered about the table for the feast, the governor inquired, "Is your father living and is he well?" They answered, "He is living and he is well." Then inquired the governor, "Is this your youngest brother of whom you told me?" and when they answered that this was their brother, Benjamin, the governor turned to him and said, "May God be gracious unto you!"

After the dinner was over the servants filled the sacks with grain. While this was being done the governor sent a secret message to his overseer, saying, "Put my own silver cup in the sack that belongs to the youngest one." The brothers, knowing nothing of this, started on their way home, rejoicing at the success of their mission. But they had not gone far when a messenger from the governor came running after them.

"One of you has taken my master's silver cup!" he cried, "and I have come to find who it is."

The brothers were amazed and alarmed. "We did not take your master's cup," they said. "Look in our sacks and you will see that we speak the truth."

When the sacks were opened, sure enough there in Benjamin's sack was the governor's silver cup. The brothers were filled with dismay as they turned sadly about and returned to the governor's house.

When they had been brought before the governor,

he gave the command, "Send everyone out from the room, and leave me alone with these men."

After the others had left the room, he astonished the brothers by turning to them and crying: "Do you not know me? I am your brother, Joseph, whom you sold into Egypt many years ago. I beg of you not to grieve over this evil thing that you did unto me, for God intended it all to work out for good. Wherefore, hasten home to my father, and tell him that I am living and well, and that I am possessed of houses and lands, and food to spare for you all. Return to me, therefore, bringing our father Jacob, and bring your households and your flocks and herds, and come and live in this land, where I am second only to the king."

Quickly did the sorrow of the brothers turn to joy as Joseph kissed each of them, in proof of his forgiveness. They hastened home to their father with the glad news, and soon returned with him and their households to live in peace and plenty in the land of Egypt. For many years they dwelt in this land under the protection of Joseph, who had forgiven the great wrong done to him many years before.

VII

REBEKAH AT THE WELL

FOR many days the little caravan had traveled over the burning sands, toward the little town of Haran. Now they had reached the gates of the city, and the tired camels sank upon their knees near the village well, where the flocks and herds came for water, and it was the hour when the women, as was the custom, came out to draw water for their household.

When, at the command of the drivers, the camels had settled themselves upon the ground, the leader of the caravan lifted his face toward heaven and said a prayer of gratitude for his safe journey. Just as he finished his prayer, a group of the village women reached the well and began to draw water. Among them was one very beautiful maiden, who carried her pitcher upon her shoulder.

When she had filled her pitcher and was carrying it dripping with cool water from the well, the stranger came forward and said to her, "Pray give me some water to drink."

The maiden, seeing how weary and tired the stranger was, took her pitcher down from her shoulder and put it to his lips, while he drank deeply to quench his thirst. Then she said, "If you will allow me, I will draw water for thy camels also, for they must be thirsty even as thou."

With this, she poured the water from her pitcher into the drinking trough, and went back to the well

33

for more water, and kept pouring into the trough until the camels had their fill.

While the maiden was busy in this way, the stranger had kept his eyes upon her, but had spoken no word. When she had finished her task he came forward to meet her and, bowing before her, he offered her as a present a beautiful golden ring and two golden bracelets.

Then the stranger said to her, "Tell me, I pray thee, to what family dost thou belong, and if there is room in thy father's house for a stranger to spend the night as he pauses in his journey." The maiden told him that her father's name was Bethuel, and said, "There is room and to spare for thee and thy camels as well."

When the stranger heard her speak these words he did what seemed to be a strange thing, he lifted his face again to heaven and gave thanks to God, saying aloud, "The Lord in his goodness has led me to the very household that my master desired me to find."

Now, to understand these strange words, you must understand that the stranger was the servant of Abraham, the leader of the Hebrews. The ten camels of the caravan were Abraham's camels, and the burdens of beautiful silks, embroideries, silver and gold, which they carried on their backs, also belonged to Abraham. Abraham had sent his servant, with the camels carrying beautiful presents, back to his old home, that he might there find a wife for Abraham's son, Isaac, from among his own people.

When the maiden had received the presents from the stranger and heard the prayer he prayed, she

ran home before him and told her mother all that
had happened. Her brother Laban then went out
by the well to find the stranger and bring him to
their home. They made the camels comfortable for
the night, and then gathered for the evening meal.

When they were at the table the stranger said,
"I will not eat until I have told you who I am and
why I have come here."

"Tell us," they said.

"I am the servant of the great Abraham, leader
of his people and friend of God. He has untold
silver and gold, flocks and herds without number.
He has men servants and maid servants and many
camels. Our people love him and are glad to obey
his word. Abraham has a son, Isaac, whom he
loves as he loves his own life. For him he would
choose a wife from among this people, who are of
his own blood and kindred.

"He has, therefore, sent me to choose out the
maiden who is most beautiful and kind, to be the
wife of his beloved son Isaac. When I was setting
out on this journey my master said to me, 'The
Lord, before whom I walk, will send his angel with
thee, and prosper thy ways.' I have, therefore,
come at his bidding to find a wife for his son Isaac,
even as he said.

"When I came to the well this evening, knowing
that I had reached the end of my journey, I prayed
this prayer to the Lord God, saying, 'O Lord, the
God of my master Abraham, if now thou do prosper
my way which I go: behold, I stand by the fountain
of water; and let it come to pass, that the maiden
which cometh forth to draw, to whom I shall say,
Give me, I pray thee, a little water of thy pitcher

to drink; and she shall say to me, 'Both drink thou, and I will also draw water for thy camels; let the same be the woman whom the Lord hath appointed for my master's son.'

"Behold, even as I finished my prayer, this beautiful maiden, even Rebekah, came down to the well, and I asked her to give me to drink. At once she gave me water and then offered to draw water for my camels as well. When she told me her father's name, behold, I knew it was the very family that my master Abraham had chosen as the one from which the wife of his son Isaac should come.

"By this I know, therefore, that the Lord God has prospered my way, and has sent his angel before my face to guide me and to help me in my search. And now I beg that you may tell me, will this beautiful maiden, even Rebekah, return with me to my master's house, even Abraham's, to make glad his heart for his son Isaac's sake?"

The father made answer, "Let the maiden speak for herself. This matter is ordered of the Lord God, and we will not stand in the way of its coming to pass, as he wills."

Rebekah said that she would go to the house of Abraham and become the wife of Isaac. Then the servants brought out all the rich presents which Abraham had sent. There were presents for Rebekah the maiden, presents for her mother and for all the family.

The next morning Rebekah's parents gave her much rich clothing, and maid-servants of her own to go with her to her own home.

The caravan arrived at the home of Abraham. Isaac was out in the field. As he saw the caravan returning, he looked, and behold, a beautiful maiden got down from her camel and came toward him, walking with a veil over her face. Quickly did Isaac go to meet Rebekah, holding out his hands to her in welcome.

Thus did Rebekah come to live in the tent of Isaac and be his wife.

VIII

TIMOTHY, THE BOY WHO FOLLOWED JESUS

It was late spring in the village of Lystra. Not far from one of the little white houses that looked almost like marble as the sun shone upon it, was the figure of a boy of nine or ten, stretched out flat on the ground under a fig tree. His white tunic was rumpled; there was a large black spot upon his left cheek, and his whole appearance was that of a boy who since the rising of the sun had been roaming through the fields and having the best time a lad could have. Just now, lying face down, resting upon his elbows, he was watching closely the insects in a big ant-hill, as they scurried about, each one busily at work on its particular task.

"Timothy! Timothy!" a sweet call sounded from the steps of the house near by. "Timothy, thou must come now and do thy lessons."

For a moment, the boy looked very cross. He had wanted to stay out and play a while longer. Then he quickly sprang to his feet and, with a cheery answer, he started back toward the house. He had remembered that on the day before his mother had promised him that on the morrow she would tell him the story of Jesus of Nazareth and his followers, who went about doing good, being kind to little children and helpful to those who were sick.

As Timothy hurried toward the house, he thought of the things some of the other boys often said, complaining about their lessons, and how they sometimes found fault with their teachers. But Timothy was fortunate, for he had the two best teachers in all of Lystra, he was sure—his mother, Eunice, and his grandmother, Lois.

Often the people in the town talked about the day when the two women had come to be followers of Jesus of Nazareth. "Surely," was the thought of many, "they will strive to make the lad, too, a follower of the Galilean."

Busy days passed in the home of Timothy. He did many things about the home; and he jumped and raced with the other lads in the town until he became the champion of them all. "He must have a strong body if he is to do his work in the world," his mother often said, and she was always glad when he was playing with his friends.

Every day, too, a certain amount of time was set aside for his lessons. Sometimes Eunice was his teacher, and sometimes he studied under his grandmother, Lois. In those days there were not nearly as many books as there are now, and they taught him mostly from the Old Testament. They spent countless hours, too, in telling him stories of Jesus of Nazareth.

As Timothy grew older he, too, loved the great Master, and he wished that he might be able to do something to show his love. "Would that I could do something big for Jesus," he confided to his mother one day. "But I can't think of anything now."

"Perhaps," his mother said, "one of the teachers

and followers of Jesus will come here some day, and thou canst talk it all over with him." She was very happy over her son's wish, and she felt sure that some day his opportunity would come.

A few years passed, and Timothy had grown to be one of the sturdiest and most upright youths in all of Lystra.

"Mother!" he burst into the house with the cry. "Mother, wilt not thou and grandmother hurry with me to the market place? They say that Paul the apostle, the disciple of Jesus, is coming, and that he is even now entering the city!"

Toward the market place the three hurried. They had hoped for so long that a great teacher would come that now they could hardly wait to see him and to hear his words of wisdom. A crowd was gathered in the square, and many people were running from all directions. "Come quickly," they called to one another. "Paul, the great teacher, has come!" Standing on an elevation, there was the stranger. Timothy could not see his face plainly, because of the throng of people.

"Ye men of Lystra," the teacher's words sounded clearly over the heads of his listeners, "have you heard of Jesus of Nazareth? He is the Messiah for whom the Hebrews have been looking for hundreds of years. Let me tell you about him, so that you too may go out and serve him."

Hardly had Paul said these words when there was a stir in the crowd. Some one was trying to push his way to the front. "It is Timothy," said one. "Ho! Timothy!" mocked a lad who had ever been jealous of Timothy's skill in their games, "art thou, too, going to become a Christian?" But

Timothy never hesitated. Straight toward Paul he made his way.

"Rabbi," his words sounded as clear as the tones of a temple bell, "rabbi, I would serve Jesus! Tell me what I may do!"

A deep hush fell upon the crowd. One or two, who had come to jeer, turned away, ashamed. On the edge of the throng, for they had not been able to force their way to the front, Eunice and Lois stood, their arms about each other. Their faces were alight with joy and thanksgiving. "Let us thank God," they murmured, "for Timothy, our son; and may God use him in his service."

For hours Paul talked with the people, telling them the story of the man of Galilee, of how he had gone about doing good, how he had finally been put to death, but was still living in the hearts of his believers. As he talked, Timothy stood by his side or sometimes he went down into the crowd and encouraged some one who was almost ready to begin to serve the Master.

Night was drawing on when Paul, placing his hand upon Timothy's shoulder, in a voice filled with praise and thankfulness, said:

"My lad, this day hast thou begun thy great work for Jesus. From now on thou shalt serve him in joy and blessedness."

And Timothy, his head bowed, silently thanked God for the joy that had come to him that day.

IX

IN HIS FATHER'S HOUSE

FOR many years Jesus had looked forward to the time when he would be old enough to go with his parents to Jerusalem to the Feast of the Passover. "When you are twelve years old," his mother and father had promised him, "you may go with us to Jerusalem." And this had made Jesus very happy.

"I shall see the caravans from Damascus," he told himself, "and surely there will be rug-makers there from Persia. Maybe I shall see some of the wise men from Egypt; perhaps I may even be able to get a scarab for my very own." Then his mind turned to the wonderful things he had been studying, and of the story he had heard so many times about the Passover night, when God had delivered the Israelites from the hand of Pharaoh. Over and over he had said to himself: "I shall go to the Temple, and perhaps I may even sit at the feet of the great teachers—if only I might do that! Then I could learn more about God, who is my heavenly Father."

At last the day came. Everyone who could possibly leave his work had made preparation to go from Nazareth to Jerusalem. Together they set out, a long, happy procession. Gay colors caught the sunlight, for everyone was wearing his best. The little children kept close to their mothers' sides, but the boys of Jesus' age, who were trustworthy and able to care for themselves, were allowed to go about, first staying with friends, at one end of the line, and then groups of lads going on swift side expeditions. There were many interesting things to be seen, and for many of them it was their first real journey away from the little hill-town of Nazareth.

To the great white and gold Temple went Jesus with his parents, after they reached the city of Jerusalem. He heard the blowing of the sacred horns announcing that the time had come for the services to begin. The choirs, chanting the psalms of David, thrilled him with their music. He watched the men of the Temple go out, with sickles and baskets, to cut the sheaf of barley that was threshed, and after being dried over a sacred fire, was ground into fine flour, and offered unto God as the first fruit of the harvest.

Then the day came when every road leading out of Jerusalem was thronged with people. The Feast of the Passover was over, and everyone was homeward bound. The pilgrims from Nazareth were in one group, and Joseph and Mary and the younger children were traveling happily along the way. It was good to have been at Jerusalem, but they were glad to be going home again.

When evening came, and the procession had stopped for the night, Mary turned to Joseph. "Isn't it strange that Jesus doesn't leave his friends and come to us?" she asked him. "He has been with them all day, but now that it is night he should come back to us." A search was made up and down the line of travelers. "Have you seen Jesus?"

anxiously the question was repeated. But everywhere came the answer, "No, he has not been with us to-day."

Then, frantic with anxiety, Mary and Joseph turned back toward Jerusalem. Mary wept as they retraced their steps, and Joseph strode on, filled with anger at himself. "To think that I, whom God chose to look after the child, should be so neglectful of my trust!" he groaned to himself. "Unfaithful! Unfaithful!"

At best, it took them a whole day to reach the city. All along the way they had searched for Jesus, but no trace of him could they find. Through the city they hunted, looking in every place where a boy might be. But when night came they had not found him. Up they rose with the dawn, and finally, they turned their steps toward the Temple, gleaming white in the sunlight.

"Hark!" Mary clutched Joseph's arm, just as they passed into the twilight of the sacred place of worship. "That sounds like the voice of Jesus!" Joseph's voice trembled with eagerness. "Can it be he?"

Quickly they passed through court and temple porch until they came to a room in which was a group of learned doctors. There in the midst of the men, eagerly listening to every word, and asking questions that were amazing in the knowledge and wisdom they showed, was Jesus.

"Son, everywhere have we sought thee with anxious hearts!" cried Mary, quickly stepping to his side. But Jesus, who had long been hoping for the time when in the Temple he could learn more about the God whom he loved as his heavenly Father, and whom he had always tried to serve, could not understand his mother's anxiety.

"But why did you search for me?" he answered. "Did you not know that I should be in my Father's house?"

X

THE FOUR FISHERMEN OF GALILEE

"Jesus is down by the Sea of Galilee! Let us go
and find him!" From lip to lip the news had flown,
until the great Teacher was surrounded by an
enormous crowd of people. Eagerly they pressed
forward to hear his wonderful words, crowding
against one another, until they had finally pushed
Jesus clear to the water's edge. Gentle little waves
lapped his feet, and still the eager multitude crowded
against him, jostling each other in their great desire
to be near the marvelous Teacher.

Turning his head, Jesus could see two boats not
very far from the shore. In them were the four
fishermen, Simon Peter, Andrew, James, and John.
They were working hard, for they were washing their
heavy nets and making ready for their next catch.
The work of a fisherman was often disagreeable and
extremely hard, but they were working with a will,
and sometimes a cheerful word or a strain of song
floated back on the breeze to the crowd on the
shore. Occasionally the four stopped for a moment
and looked back toward the group on the land, as
though wishing that they too were in the throng
about Jesus.

For those four men were not strangers to the
Master. Already they had listened to his teachings
and had talked with him, and he knew that they
were friendly toward him and his work. "Surely,"
Jesus thought, "they will be glad to make room for

me in their boat." For a moment he hesitated to call them from their task, but he knew that Simon and Andrew would be glad for a chance to help, and then, too, perhaps he could repay them later in the day for their service.

"O Simon! Simon!" Clearly the voice of Jesus sounded out over the water, through his cupped hands.

Quickly Simon and Andrew stopped their work on the net, and grasping the oars, they pulled rapidly in toward the shore.

"Simon," said the Master, "thou seest how the throng presses against me. Take me in thy boat, I pray thee, that I may more easily teach them. Wilt thou do for me this service?"

A wild flush of pride and embarrassment colored the faces of the two simple-hearted brothers. What an honor to have the Master, the Man of Galilee, whom people were calling the Messiah, in their boat! For a moment they were silent and disconcerted. Then Simon, always the more impulsive of the two, sprang to his feet in the boat, which rocked with the sudden motion.

"Master, gladly will we serve thee!" and there was such a ring of sincerity in his voice that the Teacher's face grew bright with pleasure.

Quickly the boat was shoved in on the sands. The two men, working hurriedly, shoved the nets away at one end of the craft, and carefully washing and drying the seat in the bow, that none of the slime and dirt from the nets could remain, they helped Jesus to his place.

For hours, rocking on the gently moving waves, a little distance from the shore, the great Rabbi taught the people. His sweet voice sounded melodiously across the water, and as he talked their eyes opened widely with interest, and their faces grew bright with happiness as he told them of the love of God, their heavenly Father, and that no matter what their sins, if they would only repent they would be forgiven.

Crouching in the boats, not even conscious of their cramped, uncomfortable position, the two brothers listened with rapt attention. Forgotten were the fish and their nets, their thoughts were only of Jesus.

At last the Rabbi ceased speaking and the crowd on the shore unwillingly turned away. Only for a moment, as though resting, was Jesus silent. Then, "Put out into the deep," his words came, as though it were early morning and he were eager to be at work. "Put out into the deep, and let down your nets for a catch," he said to Simon.

Hardly had the fishermen awakened from the ecstasy with which they had been listening to the Master. Shaking himself, as a man awakening from a deep sleep, Simon answered:

"Master, we toiled all night and took nothing, but at thy word I will let down the nets." And as Simon thought of the useless work of the night, there was a shade of discouragement in his voice.

Perhaps, the two men were afraid that they would have continued bad luck and that Jesus would think them poor fishermen. They did want to appear at their best in his eyes; in some way he always brought out the best qualities of those with whom he came in contact.

Willingly and with the skill of adepts, they let down their nets. Hardly had the water closed over them when there came a tug as of many fish. A look of surprise, almost of disbelief, came over the faces of the two men. They had fished right here all the night before, and now their nets were straining with the weight of the catch. For a moment Simon and Andrew, while Jesus looked quietly on, struggled with their heavy net. Then, with a murmured word, "We must have help, or we shall lose the fish," Simon beckoned to their helpers, James and John, whose boat was anchored near by, to come to their assistance.

Rapidly, with never a wasted motion, the four men worked together as one. Jesus, as he watched them, delighted in their skill and in the way in which they toiled together. As he sat there, idle for the moment, he was thinking of his own work, of how like helpless fish the men of Palestine were, and of the great need he too had for helpers. He thought of the strong bodies of the four men near him, and he delighted in the even play of their firm muscles. They were kind-hearted, too, and courteous, and how willingly Simon and Andrew had left their work when he had asked them! They had said they had fished all night, with never a catch; how patient and how industrious they were!

While these thoughts were going through the mind of the Master, the four men had succeeded in hauling in the net, part in one boat and the rest in the other, and so great and so heavy was the catch that both boats settled more deeply into the water. Amazement filled the minds of the four men; never before had they seen such a haul! Suddenly, overwhelmed with wonder and with his feeling of unworthiness, Simon threw himself down at the feet of Jesus.

"Depart from me, for I am a sinful man, O Lord!" his voice shook with emotion, and he looked pleadingly up into the Master's face.

In those moments Jesus had made his decision. These four men were to be his helpers. Bending over the kneeling Simon, his voice filled with a divine assurance, he said:

"Fear not; from henceforth thou shalt catch men." And the four fishermen knew that Jesus meant that they should have a part in his work, teaching men, and bringing them to the Master. Quickly they rowed their boats to the shore, and the Bible tells us that "they left all and followed him."

XI

HOW A SICK GIRL WAS CURED

THIS is the story of a girl who was twelve years of age, and who lived with her father and mother in a beautiful home in the country, in a far-away land and a time long ago.

It chanced that this girl became ill and her sickness grew until day by day she became weaker, and it was feared that she might never be well again. There came a time when she was so weak that she lay very white and still on her bed, with her eyelids closed, and her breathing so faint that it could scarcely be heard. Her father had left his work that day to come and sit by his daughter's bedside, for she liked to place her hand in his, and she was very sick.

Suddenly, while the father thought his daughter was asleep, she opened her eyes and said: "Father, is Jesus of Nazareth still in our town? One day before I became sick I saw him down by the market place, and he spoke to me and the other children so kindly that we all loved him and followed him. He goes about helping people, and I think he could make me well."

Now, the father had thought of this same thing himself, for he had heard how Jesus was able to heal those who were sick, and, when his daughter, after a moment of silence, again opened her eyes and whispered, "Please, father, will you not find Jesus and ask him to come and make me well," he decided to go at once and find the Master, and beg him to come and heal his daughter.

The father called the girl's mother to come and sit by her while he hurried into the town to see whether he could find where Jesus was staying. He found him in a friend's house, and approaching Jesus, cried out, "Please, Master, I fear that my daughter is dying! Will you not come quickly and lay your hands on the child, that she may live?"

Jesus arose quickly and went with the father. When the crowd saw him going along the street, many followed him, each person trying to get near enough to see him well, to look up into his face, or to hear the words he was speaking to those nearest to him.

Among those who were following him was a poor woman who, for many years, had been ill with a disease that the doctors were unable to cure. She was weak and very weary, and did not hope to get near enough to Jesus to touch his hand or to speak to him. She said to herself, "If I could even touch the hem of his garment, I am sure that I should be healed." And so, coming as close as she could, she put out her hand and touched the edge of his robe, and immediately she felt the thrill of health and life, and knew that she was healed.

Jesus, knowing that someone had touched his robe, turned about, and looking kindly at the woman, asked, "Who touched me?" Then he spoke comforting words to her, and she went on her way happy and rejoicing.

While all this was going on the father of the girl was much worried over the delay, and he spoke to Jesus: "Master, will you not please hasten, for my daughter is very ill, and she will surely die before we can reach her."

And, sure enough, the father had hardly spoken when they saw a servant running rapidly toward them. This servant came from the home of the sick girl, and said to his master, "Thy daughter is already dead. Do not trouble Jesus any more."

Jesus was sorry for the father, who began to grieve over his daughter, and said to him, "Fear not, only believe and she shall be made whole." When they reached the house, they heard sounds of sorrow and weeping. Friends and neighbors had been told that the girl had died, and the mourners had come.

Jesus came among them and said, "Weep not, for she is not dead, but sleepeth." When he had passed by, they laughed him to scorn, being sure that she was dead.

The father and mother led Jesus to the room where their daughter lay, still and breathless. Quietly and tenderly he bent over her, took her hand in his and called to her, saying, "Maiden, arise." Quickly the color came back to her cheeks. She began to breathe. Her eyes opened. She sat up in bed, and then threw her arms around her father's neck. The next moment she was out of bed, walking about, seemingly as well as ever.

Jesus told her father and mother to give her food, and soon they were sitting down to a feast together.

Neither the father nor mother nor the girl herself ever forgot their good Friend, who, when she was sick, had made her well again.

XII

JESUS AMONG HIS FRIENDS

THE pretty village of Bethany was only two miles from Jerusalem. Its small whitewashed houses shone in the sun almost like marble. In the green trees, birds hopped about from twig to branch, singing happily, and now and then a lark soared high above the fields, and its gay melody came floating down.

In one of those little white houses lived three people who were among Jesus' closest friends. Mary, Martha, and Lazarus were their names, and they were brother and sisters. Often Jesus went there, and on every occasion he was welcomed with all sorts of loving attention; Lazarus hastened to meet him; Mary had cool water brought to bathe the dust from his feet; and Martha bustled about the house, preparing a quiet room that he might rest, and delicious fruits and foods to tempt his appetite.

Frequently, after they had eaten, the four lingered long about the table. Lazarus and Jesus often discussed the affairs of the day, just as men talk of such things now. Sometimes, if Lazarus were not at home, Mary would sit for hours near Jesus, listening to him as he talked, or asking questions about many things. Martha, who was what we would call a "practical" person, was usually hurrying here and there about the house, doing everything she could think of to make her Master more comfortable. Now and then she would pause and listen for a moment to his words.

One day, when she was tired and, perhaps, everything had not gone well with her baking, she had suddenly thought, "Why doesn't Mary help me?" and, almost without thinking, she turned to Jesus, with "Lord, dost thou not care that my sister hath left me to serve alone? Bid her therefore that she help me." And Jesus saw how tired she was, so he said to her, "Martha, thou art troubled and anxious over many things. Mary has chosen the better part." And he explained to Martha that he did not care so much about having rich foods and constant attention, but that he was there to talk with them, and to rest from his hard work.

Many times Jesus visited there in Bethany. Often, perhaps, Mary and Martha invited the people of the village in to talk with their Lord. Sometimes they gave special feasts for him, and always there was great joy and happiness when he came into their home.

But one day there came a great sadness to them. Lazarus was taken very sick. Frightened, the sisters thought of their best friend, Jesus, and sent word to him by messenger, "Lord, behold, he whom thou lovest is sick." But when Jesus heard it he said, "This sickness will not end in death, but because of it many people who have hitherto doubted me will come to know and love me as never before."

Then, after two days, Jesus said to his disciples, "Let us go back to Bethany, to the home of Mary and Martha." But the disciples knew that Jesus' enemies in the region about Bethany were anxious to work out their wicked plans against him, and he was urged to stay away from the place. But Jesus said, "Our friend, Lazarus, is fallen asleep, but I go that I may awake him out of his sleep." The disciples did not know that he meant that Lazarus was dead, and they said, still trying to keep him from going to Bethany, "But, Lord, if he is asleep, surely he will recover." Then Jesus answered them plainly, "Lazarus is dead."

As Jesus and the men drew near their friends' house in Bethany, the sounds of grief came to their ears. They heard the mournful sound of the flute, and the loud wailing of the hired mourners. Martha, her face swollen from weeping, when she heard that he was coming, hurried out to meet him. Mary still sat in the house. "O, Lord," broken-heartedly Martha cried, throwing herself at Jesus' feet, "if thou hadst been here, my brother would not have died! And even now I know that whatsoever thou shalt ask of God, he will give thee."

Quickly Jesus stooped to comfort her. "Thy brother shall live again," he said. She did not understand exactly what Jesus meant, but just to have him near comforted her. Then she thought of Mary, weeping in the house, and she quickly sent a message back, saying, "The Master is here and calleth thee."

When Jesus saw Mary coming toward him, her long veil covering her face and her whole figure stooped with sorrow, he was sadly troubled. The mourners, who had followed Mary from the house, crowded about, weeping and wailing loudly.

With a whispered word of encouragement to the sisters, Jesus turned away and walked into the garden where the tomb of Lazarus was, to bring

back his friend to life and strength. Hardly any
time at all had passed, when Lazarus, a flush of
health upon his cheeks, and his eyes filled with
happiness, came forth with Jesus and joined his
sisters and their friends. Surprised, many of them
frightened, and all of them filled with awe, the
mourners turned away, and Mary and Martha and
Lazarus were left alone with their Friend.

XIII

THE BOY WHO BECAME A FRIEND OF JESUS

IT was a truly beautiful day. The sun seemed to be rising out of the Sea of Galilee, and there was a path of gold sparkling across the blue waters. Red lilies made splashes of color among the green grasses. From high above the fields there came the lilting melody of a lark, and the sparrows flitting about kept up a continuous happy prattle. In his tiny upper room a boy was dressing hurriedly, making ready for a day's outing in the country.

"Son," his mother had said the night before, "to-morrow is thy birthday, and I shall let thee do whatever thou dost wish all the day. I only ask that thou dost get into no mischief."

He had gone to bed filled with happy anticipation. Suddenly he had thought of the wonderful he had heard the men in the neighborhood him whom they called Jesus of Nazareth; had healed a blind man, how he had even back to life a girl whom everyone had belie be dead, and how kind and gentle he was w children.

"Perhaps, mother," he had suggested, chattered through his breakfast, "perhaps go north along the lake and find Jesus of N Neighbor Timothy said that he and his were near Bethsaida yesterday."

And his mother, as she watched him swinging sturdily along the shore, hurrying eagerly toward the north, his package of lunch under his arm, said a little prayer to the God of her fathers that her son might be kept safe through the day, and that he might see the wonder-working Man from Nazareth.

Along the beach hastened the boy. The way to Bethsaida was long, and the sun had already dried the dew from the grass. Now he stopped just for a moment to watch a gull dip down into the water, but after that he hurried on again twice as fast.

"What's that?" he said suddenly to himself. "It sounds like many people talking together." He left the sandy shore of the lake, and walked through the lilies until he could see the road. "Why, it's crowded with people—and what can it mean? Many of them are lame. There's a man carrying a little girl—O, they, too, have heard about Jesus of Nazareth and they are going to find him!"

With a word of greeting to a friend here and there in the group, he sped on, and soon he was near the front of the procession. As they went, people joined them from every side, and sometimes they overtook cripples, lame or blind, or so sick that they had to lie down by the side of the road to rest.

"There he is!" came the cry. "There is Jesus of Nazareth! Hail, Master!" and loving friends urged on the weary ones whose illnesses had made them lag behind. "Jesus of Nazareth is ahead just a little way and he will cure you!"

Swift as an arrow went the boy toward the crowd, in the midst of which he knew he would find Jesus. Wriggling about among the people, sliding through openings that seemed hardly large enough to let him through, around men wasted with illness and lying on pallets, past women whose pain-racked faces wore a new look of hope, clear up to the front rank of people he made his way. And then he saw Jesus!

Tall he was, and straight as the noblest cedar of Lebanon. His face, tanned by the hot suns of the desert, was more gentle even than that of the boy's own mother's as she had cared for him when he had been ill. "How strong he must be!" enviously thought the lad, looking at the strong muscles of Jesus' arms, and then he remembered that back in Nazareth Jesus had been a carpenter.

"If he would only speak to me!" wished the boy, and started to push his way nearer to the Master. But just then he saw a little girl who was so lame she could barely walk and who was struggling forward to reach the healer. So the lad stepped back, to make room for her. Hardly could he believe his eyes when he saw her turn, after the Master had taken her in his arms and touched the crippled leg, and firmly as the lad himself, go back into the crowd where her sister was waiting for her. She didn't even walk the whole distance; for, delighted by the new feeling of strength and eager to see what she could do, she covered part of the way with a hop, a skip, and a jump!

So it went all day; and Jesus taught them wonderful things and healed many who were sick. Once there came a man who for years had been sick in his mind; "possessed of demons," they called it then. With a word, Jesus had commanded the evil spirit to leave his victim, and now that man was going about in the crowd, helping those who were too ill to make way by themselves, to a place near the Master.

It seemed as though hardly an hour could have passed, when the disciples, glancing toward the west, where the sun was sinking in a blaze of crimson and orange, said, "Master, let us send the people away, for the evening has come, and they have had nothing to eat for hours."

But Jesus answered them, "They have no need to go away; give ye them to eat."

"Why, Master," they had answered, "we cannot feed them, for we have no food, and there are five thousand men here who must be fed."

"Search ye," the Master said, "and bring what food ye can find."

Straight toward the boy came Andrew, one of Jesus' followers. "Lad, what have ye there?" he said, pointing to the little package of lunch.

"Only five barley loaves and two fishes," answered the boy quickly, "but the Master may have them all."

Close beside Andrew the lad moved. After Jesus had blessed the bread, the lad heard him say, "Give to all the people who are here, and if any food is left, gather up the fragments."

Soon the disciples were back. "Everyone hath had his fill, Master," they said, "and here is what was left over." And they placed before Jesus twelve baskets filled with broken pieces!

And then we can imagine that the wonderful thing for which the lad had been wishing all day, but for which he had hardly dared hope, happened! Perhaps a strong hand was laid on his shoulder, and in his ear he heard the voice of the Master, deep and sweet as the low tones of the temple harps:

"My lad, blessed shalt thou be forever, for in giving thy loaves and thy fishes thou hast helped me in my work to-day."

XIV

THE FORGIVING FATHER

ONCE there was a father who had two sons.

"Father," said the younger son, "give me the share of the property that falls to me. I am tired of staying here and never doing anything that seems interesting. Please give me my share, and let me go into the world!"

Sadly the father bowed his head as the young man spoke. Through his mind there flashed pictures of the happy life he and his wife and the two boys had enjoyed. He saw the two curly-haired lads as they looked back in the days when they had been children. But finally when he was convinced of the boy's earnestness, he portioned out to him his share. "Go, my son," he gave him his blessing, "and may the Lord be with thee."

Gaily the young man traveled along the dusty roads toward the far country that was his goal. "At last I shall see the world!" he had told his elder brother as he started on his journey.

Sometimes, as the youth passed through small towns and villages, he would stop and join the young men in their good times. He bought many rich robes for himself, and other things to add to the pleasure of his journey. Sometimes he threw handfuls of silver to the beggars, just to see them fight and scramble for the coins.

At last he reached the distant country he had so wanted to see. He was fascinated by the strange sights, the peculiar customs, and the picturesque clothing of the people. He spent long hours in the market place, buying many things which interested him. His wealth and generosity brought a large number of young men about him, and he gave many a merry party to his new friends. "At last," he thought, "I am perfectly happy." And he was so happy that he forgot all about his father and brother at home.

It was not long before things changed. A famine was in the land, and both cattle and people were dying for lack of food. Days, weeks, and months had passed with never a drop of rain to moisten the parched earth. Heat waves shimmered above the yellow sands. Slowly the corn dropped on its stalks, until no living plants were left. People who had been wise enough to store up food against a famine, ate sparingly of what they had saved; great prices were charged for food in the market places. Everywhere the people suffered.

During all those days the young stranger had been living joyfully and thoughtlessly. Each party that he gave was more magnificent and costly than any of the others. More and more friends had gathered about him, and he was always the central figure in their good times. But one morning his servant came to him and said:

"O, master, give me, I pray thee, more money that I may buy food and pay the wages of thine other servants. Thou knowest of the famine, and the high cost of everything which we need."

"Go to the hiding place," was the reply of the young man, "and bring me what money thou findest there."

Hardly had the servant left his master before he was back again; his face was pale with fear.

"O, master," tremblingly he spoke, "thine hiding place is empty. There is not even a single piece of silver there!"

Days of misery, of want, of actual starvation, dragged slowly by. The young man's friends deserted him, one by one, until he was left alone. Driven by desperation, he at last hired himself out to one of the citizens of that country. It seemed that his misfortune was complete when he was commanded to feed the swine, and he was so hungry that he would have liked to eat the husks himself.

Then, one day, the Bible tells us, he came to himself. "How many hired servants of my father's have bread enough and to spare, and I perish here with hunger!" he thought. "I will arise and go to my father, and will say unto him, 'Father, I have sinned against heaven and in thy sight; I am no more worthy to be called thy son; make me as one of thy hired servants!'" Thus he planned what he would say to his father, as he slowly struggled over the long miles back to his home. At last he drew near his home, dusty, and so weary he could hardly drag himself along.

On up the road he came, dragging one foot after the other, and looking neither to right nor to left. But his father saw him and ran forward eagerly, his hands outstretched.

"My son! My son! At last you have returned!" and the father threw his arms about the boy.

"Father, I have sinned, and I am no more worthy to be called thy son," the penitent man started his confession. But his father interrupted him, and turned to the servants. "Fetch a ring for his finger, and shoes for his feet," he commanded, "and bring him a cloak that he may clothe himself. Then go, and prepare a fatted calf, that we may make merry. For this my son was lost, and he has returned again!"

XV

SHARING THE LAST MEAL

IT had not rained in Israel for many months. There was a great famine in the land. The brooks and creeks and rivers had nearly all dried up. There were no flowers, or gardens, or fields of barley and wheat.

The pastures, too, were scorched by the rays of the hot sun. No more did the happy shepherds lead their flocks into the sunny fields beside the quiet waters, for there were no flocks and herds.

But there was a prophet in the land of Israel at that time, by the name of Elijah. He lived alone by a small brook called Cherith. It is said that the ravens brought him bread in the morning and meat in the evening, and he drank water from the brook. But after awhile even the brook dried up, for there had been no rain in the land, and the ravens no longer brought him food.

After many days God sent a messenger to Elijah telling him to go to a nearby city where he would find food to eat and water to drink. When Elijah arrived at the gate of the city he saw a woman gathering sticks of wood, as if to build a fire. Now it happened that she was a widow, and she and her only son lived together in a small house just inside the city wall. They, too, were suffering for want of food and water. They had not had much food to eat for a long time.

67

"Good woman," said Elijah, "I am very thirsty. Will you please go and bring me water to drink?" Forgetting how faint and hungry she was, the poor widow went as fast as she could to get the water. Even though Elijah was a stranger to her, she wanted to be kind and courteous to him.

"I am very hungry also," he said. "Will you please bring me food to eat?" But then the woman hesitated, and a troubled look came over her face.

"I have no bread," she answered, "and there is but a handful of meal in the jar and a little oil in the jug. I was just ready to make a fire to prepare the bread for myself and my son, that we might eat it and die."

"Fear not," said Elijah, "our God will provide food for us. Make a cake for me first, and afterward make cakes for you and your son also."

The poor widow did not know how this was possible, since there was only enough meal for two small cakes. But even so, she was willing to divide the last of the meal with a stranger, who was also hungry.

So she went and did as Elijah had asked her, making cakes for him and her son and herself, and never again throughout the days of the famine did they want for food or for water. Because she had been kind to a stranger, her own needs had been supplied.

One day while Elijah was still there the widow's only son became very sick. In fact he was so sick that he scarcely seemed to breathe. In great distress she came to Elijah bearing her son in her arms, thinking that he was dead.

Bitterly the mother cried out to Elijah, "What

have I to do with thee, O thou man of God. Thou
art come unto me to bring my sin to remembrance,
and to slay my son."

But Elijah answered, "Give me thy son." And
he took the boy in his arms and carried him upstairs to his own room.

Then he prayed, "O Jehovah my God, hast thou
also brought evil upon the widow with whom I
sojourn. O Jehovah, let this child's soul come unto
him again."

Jehovah answered Elijah's prayer. For slowly the
boy began to breathe stronger and stronger, and he
opened his eyes, and smiled as if he were glad to see
his friend Elijah.

When Elijah came down the stairs from his room,
carrying the boy in his arms, he presented him to his
mother alive and well, saying, "See, thy son liveth."

The poor widow was so thankful that she fell
down on the ground before the prophet Elijah, to
give him thanks, saying, "Now I know that thou
art the man of God, that the word of Jehovah in
thy mouth is truth."

XVI

THE PRINCE WHO SOUGHT HAPPINESS

"DID you see which way he whom they call Jesus of Nazareth went?" The question was asked of a rug merchant in the market place by a young man who had just come hurriedly from the Temple. "Rabbi," came the answer as the merchant bowed low, "he has just passed with his disciples," and he pointed toward the east. "It may be that he is going to the Sea of Galilee, for they say he often goes there to rest and to talk with his followers."

Quickly the young man turned his steps toward the Sea. As he went, his rapid footsteps stirred up clouds of dust. Men and women stepped aside to allow him to pass, for they saw his haste, and besides, he was a ruler in the Temple. Usually, to be sure, an older man was given this position, for it was his task to take care of the service and to appoint those who should preach and read the Scriptures. But this young man, because of his noble character and great virtue, had been honored when he was quite young by being lifted to the coveted place of leadership.

"Surely this man can help me," he was thinking, as he hurried on. "All these years since I was a lad I have kept the laws and the commandments, but some way I am not satisfied. Perhaps the Galilean can tell me what more I should do. Would that I had talked with him many days ago!"

He turned a corner, and there, far ahead of him, he saw a group of men, moving slowly along, and seeming to be deep in conversation. "That is he!" he thought, and his steps grew more rapid. Once he saw three or four children run eagerly toward the little group of men. Their happy laughter floated back to him, as he saw the Master stoop to talk with them. "I wonder what he is saying," he thought, and almost jealously he wished that he were near enough to hear the conversation.

Just as he had almost reached the disciples, he was delayed by a man whom he had seen come limping upon crutches from a house beside the road. For a moment he had stood talking with Jesus; the Master had made some movement, the ruler could not see what; and now the man was coming, jumping and leaping and running along the road. Straight toward the young ruler he came.

"Behold!" he shouted, "the Master has taken away my lameness! This is the first time I have ever walked as other men. Thanks be unto God!" and in his delight he grasped the young man's hand and would hardly let him go.

At last the ruler reached Jesus and his disciples. Forgetting all about his rich garments, the young man knelt in the dust of the road before the great Teacher.

"Good Master," he begged, "tell me what I must do to gain greatest happiness."

"Why do you call me good, and ask me what to do?" Jesus responded. "God is good, and you know his commandments. Keep these if you wish to live forever: Do not kill, Do not steal, Do not bear false witness, Honor your father and your mother, Love your neighbor as yourself."

"Master," replied the young man, "I have kept

these commandments ever since I was a child. What more must I do?"

Then Jesus looked deep into the ruler's face. He saw there sincerity, honesty of purpose, and a real desire to achieve the best things in life, and he could not help loving the young man. Then he noticed the handsome garments which the ruler wore, and the heavy golden ornaments. "I am afraid," Jesus said to himself, "that this young man cares more about his money and the recognition and service he can command because of it, than he really cares about serving others. If he will only give his wealth in the service of others, he will gain the greatest happiness."

Then, with a look of great sympathy upon his face, for he knew he was asking the young man to do the hardest thing in the world, Jesus said:

"There is only one more thing that you need to do. Sell all that you own, your houses and your lands and all your great possessions, and then give your money to the poor. Come then, and follow me, and you shall find the greatest happiness in serving others."

In surprise and perplexity the young man turned away, for he had not thought that Jesus would ask him to do this thing. He did not know what to do. He sincerely wanted to find the greatest happiness, but he had never expected that he would have to give up his riches in order to gain it. If he had only been asked to build a temple, how willingly he would have done it! But to give up all that he owned and to become a poor man was too hard, and he could not make up his mind to do it.

He knew that Jesus was still standing there, looking at him with deep compassion. He tried to speak to the Master, but no words would come to his lips. At last, sadly, with hanging head, and shoulders drooping in dejection, he turned away. As he started slowly back through the dusty road, he could feel the Master's eyes still upon him, as he thought of the price he would have to pay for the greatest happiness, and we may hope that he breathed to himself, "Truly hath the Master spoken," as the new hope came to him. "I shall pray unceasingly for the strength to do as he commanded."

XVII

THREE MIGHTY MEN OF VALOR

DAVID was king over Israel, and greatly beloved by his people. In his army were thirty men who had done such great deeds that David chose them as his bodyguard. He made them his close friends.

These men could shoot an arrow or hurl a spear and hit the mark every time. Some of them had dared to fight a whole band of David's enemies, and had killed many and put the rest to flight. Mighty men of valor the Bible calls them, and they loved their king and were true to him, because he, too, was a mighty man of valor.

It happened that one year, when the harvest was ripe, some of David's enemies marched into the fields near his old home. They were ready to steal the grain, which belonged to the people of Bethlehem.

David and his men made up their minds to drive the thieves away and protect homes and crops. So they went down into the country where the enemy was stationed, and made their camp in a cave where David lived when, years before, he was being hunted by King Saul.

The days were long and hot, there was little water, and often David and his followers must have been very thirsty and tired. David longed, too, to save his old home and to punish the marauders and drive them from the fields where he used to play as a boy.

One day when he was suffering most from thirst

he thought of the old well by the gate of Bethlehem. It seemed as if no water could be quite as cold and fresh as that water. So David looked at the fields, filled with his enemies, that lay between his cave and Bethlehem, and wished out loud. "O," he said, "that one would give me water to drink of the well of Bethlehem, which is by the gate!"

Like many of our wishes, he never thought of having this one come true. But three of his strongest men heard the words of the king; and when night came on they girded on their swords, crept out of their cave, and at the risk of their lives made their way through the enemy to the well. There they filled their pitchers with cool water, and stole back past the sleeping enemies to their friends.

When David saw the water, and knew that his three mighty men had risked their lives to bring it to him, how he must have loved them! That water was more precious now than its weight in gold, because it meant the love and service of his friends. It seemed to David that the water was too precious even to drink. It would have been like drinking the lives of his three brave knights.

So he held it up in his hands and prayed, saying, "Be it far from me, O God, that I should drink this. Shall I drink the blood of the men that went in danger of their lives?" Then he poured it upon the thirsty ground, trying in this way to give it as a sacred gift to God.

What became of the three mighty men of valor we do not know. But we love to tell their story, because they were great enough to do, with courage and cheer, a hard thing which their king wished but did not ask.

XVIII

THE GOOD SAMARITAN

THERE lived in the city of Jericho a man who was so friendly and kind that his neighbors called him the "Good Samaritan." One morning the Good Samaritan, riding on his patient donkey, passed out through the gates of Jericho. They were on their way to the great city of Jerusalem, which lay about twenty miles distant. Slowly they made their way over the ascending plain which led to the mountain pass through which they must go.

As they entered the mountains the road became more rugged. At places it clung to the mountainside where cliffs rose above the travelers and where chasms yawned below. Here and there sharp turns were required, and great bowlders jutted out, completely shutting from view the road ahead.

The trip over this part of the way was always a dangerous one, for robbers frequently lurked in the dark places behind the rocks or hid in the caves on the mountainside. Many a traveler had been suddenly fallen upon and beaten by thieves and his money taken from him. Many a victim had been stripped of his raiment as well as his purse and left to suffer or die by the wayside.

"I don't like the kind of company we are apt to have," he thought, "but we will be ready for them if they appear." With this we can imagine that he swung around so it would be within easy reach a stout cudgel, which he had fastened to the saddle.

He felt for the well-filled pocketbook, and put it in a more safe place. Then he urged the donkey into a faster pace.

Suddenly, at a sharp turn of the road just ahead, he caught a glimpse of a man approaching. He grasped his club and made ready in case the man should prove to be a robber. But no! Greatly to his relief, the traveler proved to be only a priest on his way to Jericho. The Good Samaritan would have given him greeting, but the priest haughtily turned away his head and passed by on the other side; for the priests did not like the Samaritans.

At the next bend in the road he met another man, but this man was not a robber either. He was a Levite coming down from Jerusalem. The Levite, like the priest, offered no greeting, but passed by with a haughty look.

One more turn of the rugged road and the Good Samaritan would come to the most dangerous spot of all. Here the road was full of stones and the way was narrow and winding. If he could pass this point safely, he would feel that the danger was past. It would then be but a few miles to an inn where he could find rest and food.

So he went very carefully as he approached the dangerous place. His ears were alert for the slightest sound and his eye keen for signs of robbers. He thought he heard a cry ahead, and paused to listen. But no further sound came and he proceeded. Almost immediately he came to a place where marks on the ground showed that there had been a struggle. Then suddenly, a few steps farther along, he was startled and shocked by a gruesome sight. On the ground lay a man, quite

senseless and seemingly dead. His face and body
were bruised and cut, and blood was running from
his many wounds.

The Good Samaritan thought quickly. What
should he do? The robbers might be near at hand
waiting for another victim. If he went on as fast
as he could without stopping, he could escape; if
he delayed to help the injured man, the thieves
might rob him of his money, or even take his life.

He did not hesitate. He slipped off his donkey
and came to the wounded man, who was now moan-
ing with pain. He knelt beside him and examined
his wounds. Then he tenderly bound them up,
pouring in oil and wine to cleanse them and stop
the pain. After a little he lifted the sufferer onto
the back of his donkey, and walked beside him,
supporting him till they came to the inn. There
they took him in and cared for him. When the
Good Samaritan was leaving the next day to con-
tinue his journey, he paid the wounded man's bill,
telling the innkeeper to let him stay until he was
well, and that the Good Samaritan would pay whatever extra expense there was when he returned.

Nothing more is told us about the Good Samaritan, who went on his way rejoicing after he had
cared for the man by the wayside. Perhaps he
himself did not say much about the good deed
done to the man who had fallen among the robbers,
but Jesus heard of it from some one. This is the
way Jesus told the story:

A certain man was going down from Jerusalem to Jericho; and he fell among robbers,
which both stripped him and beat him, and

departed, leaving him half dead. And by chance a certain priest was going down that way: and when he saw him, he passed by on the other side. And in like manner a Levite also, when he came to the place, and he saw him, passed by on the other side. But a certain Samaritan, as he journeyed, came where he was: and when he saw him, he was moved with compassion, and came to him, and bound up his wounds, pouring on them oil and wine; and he set him on his own beast, and brought him to an inn, and took care of him. And on the morrow he took out two pence, and gave them to the host, and said, "Take care of him; and whatsoever thou spendest more, I, when I come back again, will repay thee." (Luke 10. 30–35.)

XIX

FOUR KNIGHTS OF HEROIC SERVICE

So many people came to Peter's house that it was soon filled to overflowing. When there was no longer any room inside they gathered about the door, and then filled the yard in front of the house. They kept on coming and coming, bringing with them their sick friends. They were all trying to get near Jesus, who was a guest in Peter's home that day.

There lived in Capernaum at that time a very helpless man. He was paralyzed so that he could not walk. It may be that he could not even talk. He had to lie on his bed day after day and was not able to help himself. His friends had to wait on him and do everything for him.

When they heard that Jesus was in Peter's house, they began to wonder if he could not do something for this poor, crippled man. It was not long before they were on their way to Jesus, carrying the palsied man in a strong blanket. It was hard work, but they were glad to do a good turn for their friend.

When they reached the house there were so many people about the door and in the yard that they could not get near where Jesus was. It seemed impossible to reach Jesus, so great was the throng about the house.

But they were determined to see him. They kept right on and made their way through the crowd to a side stairway that led up to the roof of the little one-story house. Up the stairway they climbed,

carefully bearing the sick man. When they reached
the top, they laid him down on the flat roof.

Then they did a strange thing. They began to tear
a hole in the roof above where Jesus was standing.
They worked away while Jesus was talking to the
people below. Soon they had the hole large enough.

They tied ropes to the corners of the blanket on
which the sick man lay, and then they carefully
picked him up and began to let him down through
the hole in the roof!

Great was the surprise of the people below when
they saw the strong arms of these four men gently
letting the sick man down into the room where
Jesus was.

Jesus stopped speaking. He turned and looked
at the man, then he looked up at his friends. He
saw at once that the four men believed that he
could heal their friend. Jesus saw that the sick
man had done things that were wrong, and wished
very much to be forgiven as well as healed.

Jesus then said to him, "My son, your sins are
forgiven." After he had spoken to the people, he
turned to the young man and said, "Rise, I tell
you, take up your blanket and go home."

The people were astonished at what happened.
For right before their eyes the palsied man arose
and took up his blanket. They made way for him
and he walked out of Peter's house a new man.
He was now well and strong.

He had to be carried to Jesus by his faithful
friends, now he was able to walk home without any
help. How glad his four friends must have been
for the part they had. How thankful the young
man was for his four friends.

XX

NEHEMIAH AND HIS COUNTRY

LONG years ago the King of Persia with a mighty army captured the Holy City, Jerusalem. The great stone wall was broken down and the strong wooden gates were burned. Homes were laid in ruin and people had to fear for safety. Many of them were taken captive back to the land of Persia.

Among the captives was a young man, Nehemiah, who found such favor in the eyes of the king that he was made one of the king's cup-bearers. Nehemiah delighted in his new duties and would have been quite happy and secure in the king's court had not his brother come from Jerusalem to visit him, bringing sad news.

"Jerusalem, the Holy City, lies in ruin," he said. "Our people are in great distress. The wall has never been repaired, nor the gates rebuilt. Our homes are destroyed. Our enemies disturb us and give us no peace. Even robbers lurk around in the ruins and wild animals prowl through the streets."

This news filled Nehemiah with such sorrow that he wept. He prayed to Jehovah to send help and deliverance to his people and longed to go back to Jerusalem that he might help to rebuild the Holy City.

One day when he felt that he could no longer stay away from his beloved people, he went before the presence of the king and said, "O king, if it please thee, let thy servant return to Jerusalem, that I may rebuild the city where my forefathers lived. My people are in great distress. They suffer hunger and hardship. There is no one to help them. O king, if I have found favor in thy sight, may it please thee to send me back to my people."

And the king answered, "Thou mayest go, O faithful servant, and for thy journey will I give unto thee money and soldiers. I pray thee return when thou hast finished thy work."

It was with a glad heart that Nehemiah, with his company of officers and horsemen, set out on the journey to Jerusalem. For many days they traveled before they finally reached the Holy City, where all Nehemiah's friends came out to greet him.

Several days passed before Nehemiah told his people why he had come. This he kept secret, for he first wanted to examine the city and complete all of his plans.

In the Bible it tells us: "After I had been there three days, I rose in the night together with a few of my followers. I told no one what my God had put in my heart to do for Jerusalem, and I had no animal with me except the one upon which I rode.

"I investigated carefully the walls of Jerusalem which were broken down and where the city gates had been destroyed by fire. I went on to the Fountain Gate and to the King's Pool, but there was no place for the animal on which I rode to pass.

"I also went up in the night along the Brook Kedron and examined the wall; then I turned back and entered by the Valley Gate. The rulers did not know where I went or what I did, for I had not as yet told my plans to the Jews or to the priests or the nobles or to the rulers.

"Finally I said to them, 'You see the bad condition in which we are, how Jerusalem lies in ruins and its gates are destroyed by fire. Come, let us rebuild the wall of Jerusalem, that we may no longer fear our enemies.'

"I told them too how my God had kindly cared for me and the words which the king had spoken to me. They said, 'Let us go to work and build.' So they entered heartily into the good work."

They all solemnly promised to follow their great leader, and that very day they began their task.

They were all eager to have a part in it. Even some of the women helped and the boys and girls who were old enough did their share. Everyone worked together under Nehemiah their leader, some on one part of the wall, some on another, and still others on the great wooden gates.

It was not an easy task to put all the stones in place. The wall to be built was very high, very wide, and very long. It extended all the way around the city, but soon the workers began to see it rise from the ruins.

There were enemies living in towns nearby who did not like to see the walls of Jerusalem being rebuilt. First they made fun of the Jews and said, "What are these feeble Jews doing? Will they complete the work in a day? Will they recover the stones from the heaps of rubbish even after they have been destroyed by fire?"

Nehemiah and his helpers kept right on working. Every day they saw the wall grow higher and longer. The clinking of the stones and the sound of the hammer was music to their ears. All the time they were thinking how safe and secure their homes would be.

When Nehemiah's enemies saw that the walls of Jerusalem were really being rebuilt, they no longer jeered, but became very angry and secretly planned to attack the workers with swords and spears and other weapons.

But Nehemiah was not afraid, even though some of his workers were. He said: "Do not fear. Remember that Jehovah our God is with us. Fight for your relatives, your sons, your daughters, your wives and your homes."

So Nehemiah set apart some of the men as guards, who were to watch while the others worked.

When the enemies heard that Nehemiah and his band kept right on working, with their swords and spears where they could reach them, they were afraid to attack them.

It took just fifty-two days to finish the wall, and to repair the gates, and Nehemiah said, "When our enemies heard that the walls of the city had been rebuilt all the surrounding nations were afraid, for they knew that this work had been done with the help of our God."

And when the work was finished, the Jews held a great feast and all the people rejoiced that their homes were once more safe. They gave thanks to Jehovah, their God who had helped them, and had sent unto them Nehemiah, to be their leader.

XXI

ELISHA AND A GREAT GENERAL

NAAMAN, captain of the hosts of Syria's army,
was a great man and much honored because he had
won many victories for his master. But Naaman
was very sorrowful; for he had become a leper, and
for his dreadful disease the doctors could find no
cure.

Now there had been brought captive by the
Syrians, from the land of Israel, a little Hebrew
maid who waited on Naaman's wife.

This maid was much distressed when she saw how
sorrowful were Naaman and all his friends, because
he had a disease which could not be cured. She told
her mistress that there lived a prophet in Samaria
who would be able to cure her master of his leprosy.

When the King of Syria heard of this he said, "I
will send a letter unto the King of Israel. I will
have Naaman bring to him rich presents of gold
and silver and changes of raiment. I will ask him
to cure Naaman of his leprosy."

So Naaman departed to journey to the King of
Israel, and he took with him ten talents of silver
and six thousand pieces of gold, and ten changes
of raiment.

When the King of Israel had read the letter which
Naaman brought to him, he was much disturbed,
and rent his clothes. "Am I able to kill and make
alive, that this man doth send unto me to recover

his servant of his leprosy?" asked the king. "None can cure of the leprosy, and behold the King of Syria but seeketh a quarrel against me."

Now Elisha, a prophet of God, heard how Naaman had come to the King of Israel, and how the king was unable to cure him.

"Wherefore hast thou rent thy clothes, and why art thou troubled?" said Elisha. "Let now this man come to me and he shall know that there is a prophet in Israel."

So Naaman came to Elisha with his horses and his chariots, and stood at the door of Elisha, desiring to be cured of his leprosy.

Elisha sent a messenger to him saying, "Go and wash in the Jordan seven times, and thy flesh shall come to thee, and thou shalt be clean."

But Naaman was angry, and went away, and said, "Behold, I expected that he would come out to me and call upon the name of the Lord his God, and wave his hand over the place which is sore of leprosy, and cure me. Are not the rivers in my own country better than the waters of Israel? Why then should I make this journey to be scorned?" And he turned and went away in anger.

And his servant came to Naaman and said, "If the prophet had bid thee do some great thing, would thou not have done it? How much rather, then, ought you to obey him when he says unto thee, 'Wash and be clean.'"

So Naaman went down and dipped himself seven times in the Jordan as Elisha had commanded him. And behold! his flesh became again like the flesh of a little child, and he was cured of his leprosy. Naaman, when he came up out of the water, said,

"Behold! Now I know that there is no god in all the earth but the God of Israel."

Then Naaman offered Elisha a present, because he had cured him of his leprosy. But Elisha would take no pay for his service. When Naaman had urged him, Elisha again refused, and Elisha said unto him, "Go in peace," and sent him back, cured of his leprosy, to his own country and people.

XXII

THE CHAMPION CHRISTIAN SOLDIER

THE command, "Forward! March!" was given;
and two hundred soldiers, two hundred spearmen
and seventy horsemen were on the move. They
were under the marching orders of the commander
of the Roman troops at Jerusalem. Cæsarea, a city
sixty miles away, was to be reached in double-quick
time.

Among the horsemen there rode a man whom
the soldiers were guarding and who was not himself
a soldier. This man was dressed as an ordinary
citizen. He had gray hair, gray beard, dark piercing
eyes and a firm but kindly countenance. He was
small in body, but dignified in appearance, and as
brave as any soldier that ever lived.

Paul, for that was his name, bore upon his body
the scars of severe beatings at the hands of officers,
rioters, and enemies of many lands. He had traveled
in many countries, preached in their cities, caused
thousands of people to become followers of Jesus,
and founded scores of churches in all parts of Asia
Minor and Europe. Paul did not fight with spear
and shield, but he was the champion Christian
soldier of his day.

And it was no easy task. "Five times," he tells
us, "I received from the Jews thirty-nine lashes.
Three times I have been beaten with rods. Once I
was stoned. Three times I have been shipwrecked.

I have been adrift at sea for a day and a night. I have traveled far and wide. I have been in dangers from rivers and robbers, in dangers from my own countrymen and from foreigners, in dangers in city and desert, in dangers on the sea and among false brothers. I have endured toil and hardship. I have passed many a sleepless night. I have endured hunger and thirst. Many a time have I been without food. I have been cold and ill-clad."

And now Paul was under arrest and leaving Jerusalem with a heavy bodyguard of Roman soldiers. This is the way it had all happened: Two days before this he was going into the Temple to worship accompanied by several of his friends. Some of his enemies were in the Temple and caught sight of him. Immediately they cried, "Help! Men of Israel, help!" and with that they seized him and dragged him out of the Temple.

A few minutes more and Paul would have been killed. As quick as a flash some one sent a message to the commander whose office was near the Temple. Soldiers rushed in among the rioters and rescued Paul from their cruel hands.

"Who is he and what has he done?" asked the commander. Some cried one thing and some another. Unable to learn what was the charge against Paul, the officer led him away to the soldiers' quarters and placed him under guard.

Later, the commander learned that a band of men had vowed not to eat or sleep until they had killed Paul. So with the strong bodyguard of Roman soldiers the great Apostle to the Gentiles was now out of Jerusalem and beyond the reach of his enemies.

Paul was taken to the city of Cæsarea, where he was called before the court. His enemies came all the way from Jerusalem to witness against him; but they were false witnesses and each one told a different story. So the governor said to Paul, "Are you willing to go up to Jerusalem and appear in the court before me there?"

Paul replied, "I am standing before the emperor's court where I ought to be tried, but if there is no truth in any of their charges against me, then no man has the power to deliver me to them."

Then Paul demanded that since he was a Roman citizen, the governor should send him to Rome to be tried in the emperor's court.

"You have appealed to the emperor," said Festus the governor, "to the emperor you shall go."

This decision meant a trip of many hundred miles across the great Mediterranean Sea, in order to reach Rome, then the most noted city in the world.

When the day came to start, an officer by the name of Julius was put in charge of Paul and some other prisoners who were on the ship. The ship on which they sailed stopped at a place called Sidon. Years before this Paul had preached at Sidon and had founded a church there. Julius was kind to Paul and let him go ashore and visit his friends while the ship lay in the harbor.

From Sidon the vessel made its way to Crete, a large island out in the middle of the Mediterranean Sea about half way to Rome. It was getting late in the season and the sea at times was very rough. Paul advised the captain to remain in that harbor until spring. "Men," he said, "I see this voyage is

going to be attended with great hardship and serious
loss not only to the cargo and the ship but also to
our own lives."

But the captain would not heed Paul's advice.
He weighed anchor and set sail, thinking he could
reach another harbor not far away where the ship
could be docked for the winter.

The day was calm and they were sailing along the
coast of Crete, when all of a sudden down rushed a
terrific hurricane and threatened to founder the ship.
So severe was the storm that the ship could not
make headway against it. They were then forced
to haul in the sails and let the boat drift.

"For many days," writes Luke, who was a friend
of Paul's and who was with him on the journey,
"neither sun nor stars could be seen, and the storm
raged heavily, and at last we had to give up all
hope of being saved." When they had gone without food for a long time Paul stood up among them
and said, "Men, you should have listened to me and
spared yourselves this hardship and loss by refusing
to set sail from Crete. I bid you cheer up. There
will be no loss of life, only of the ship. For last
night an angel of the God I belong to and serve,
stood before me, saying, 'Have no fear, Paul; you
must stand before Cæsar and God has granted you
the lives of all your fellow-voyagers.' Cheer up,
men! I believe God; I believe it will turn out just
as I have been told. However, we are to be stranded
on an island."

From this time Paul was looked upon as the
head officer of the ship. On the fourteenth night
the sailors saw signs of land. They measured the
depth of the sea and found it but nineteen fathoms.

Later on in the night they took another sounding and found only fifteen fathoms. So they anchored the ship, and anxiously waited until morning.

At daybreak the passengers still despaired of their lives. It seemed to them impossible ever to reach the land in safety, but Paul spoke words of cheer to them. "For fourteen days," he said, "you have been on the watch all the time, without a proper meal. Take some food, then, I beg of you. You are going to be saved! Not a hair of your heads will perish." Then he took a loaf of bread, gave thanks, and in their presence began to eat. And they all took food and were strengthened and cheered.

When it became light enough to see they discovered not far away a large creek with a sandy beach. They cut away the anchors, hoisted a sail to the breeze and headed for the shore. But before they reached their goal the ship struck a reef and the prow was jammed fast in the ground, and it was not long until the stern was broken to pieces by the fury of the waves.

The captain ordered those who could swim to jump overboard first and get to land, while the rest were to manage with planks or pieces of wreckage. In this way it turned out that the whole company got safe to land. What Paul had said came true. The ship was beaten to pieces by the waves, but not one of the passengers was lost.

They found that they were stranded on an island by the name of Malta. Strange as it may seem, the ship which had drifted on the waves for fourteen days and nights without a pilot had traveled in a straight course for Rome. The natives of the island showed them great kindness, and gave them food, clothing, and shelter.

Paul preached to the islanders and told them about Jesus. Many of them had never heard the story before and they believed his message and became Christians.

After three months a ship came by Malta and picked up all of the stranded passengers and landed them safe in Rome, the place where Paul had long desired to come and preach. He was met here by a little company of Christians who had heard before he arrived that he was on the way. When he saw them he thanked God and took courage.

It seems that Paul remained in Rome, practically a prisoner, the rest of his life. He was not kept in prison but was permitted to live in his own rented house, a Roman soldier keeping guard over him. For two whole years Paul lived in this house writing letters to all the churches which he had founded and telling as many people as came to him about Jesus the Christ.

The Bible does not tell us what finally happened to Paul. The story of his life ends at this point, but it is safe to say that to the end of his life he kept on telling the story about Jesus his Master.

When he finally ended his life's journey he could truthfully say, "I have fought the good fight, I have finished the course, I have kept the faith; henceforth there is laid up for me a crown of righteousness."

PART II. CHARACTER STORIES

I

THE KNIGHTS OF THE SILVER SHIELD

THERE was once a splendid castle in a forest, with great stone walls and a high gateway, and turrets that rose away above the tallest trees. The forest was dark and dangerous, and many cruel giants lived in it; but in the castle was a company of knights, of the country, to help travelers who might be in the forest, and to fight with the giants whenever they could.

Each of these knights wore a beautiful suit of armor and carried a long spear, while over his helmet there floated a great red plume that could be seen a long way off by any one in distress. But the most wonderful thing about the knights' armor was their shields. They were not like those of other knights, but had been made by a great magician who had lived in the castle many years before. They were made of silver, and sometimes shone in the sunlight with dazzling brightness; but at other times the surface of the shields would be clouded as though by a mist, and one could not see his face reflected there as he could when they shone brightly.

Now, when each young knight received his spurs and his armor, a new shield was also given him from among those that the magician had made; and when the shield was new its surface was always cloudy and dull. But as the knight began to do service against the giants, or went on expeditions to help poor travelers in the forest, his shield grew brighter and brighter, so that he could see his face reflected in it. But if he proved to be a lazy or cowardly knight, and let the giants get the better of him, or did not care what became of the travelers, then the shield grew more and more cloudy, until the knight became ashamed to carry it.

But this was not all. When any one of the knights fought a particularly hard battle and won the victory, or when he went on some hard errand for the lord of the castle and was successful, not only did his silver shield grow brighter, but when one looked into the center of it he could see something like a golden star shining in its very heart. This was the greatest honor that a knight could achieve, and the other knights always spoke of such a one as having "won his star." It was usually not till he was pretty old and tried as a soldier that he could win it. At the time when this story begins, the lord of the castle himself was the only one of the knights whose shield bore the golden star.

There came a time when the worst of the giants in the forest gathered themselves together to have a battle against the knights. They made a camp in a dark hollow not far from the castle, and gathered all their best warriors together, and all the knights made ready to fight them. The windows of the castle were closed and barred; the air was full of the noise of armor being made ready for use; and the knights were so excited that they could scarcely rest or eat.

Now there was a young knight in the castle named Sir Roland, who was among those most eager for the battle. He was a splendid warrior, with eyes that shone like stars whenever there was anything to do in the way of knightly deeds. And although he was still quite young, his shield had begun to shine enough to show plainly that he had done bravely in some of his errands through the forest. This battle, he thought, would be the great opportunity of his life. And on the morning of the day when they were to go forth to it, and all the knights assembled in the great hall of the castle to receive the commands of their leaders, Sir Roland hoped that he would be put in the most dangerous place of all so that he could show what knightly stuff he was made of.

But when the lord of the castle came to him, as he went about in full armor giving his commands, he said: "One brave knight must stay behind and guard the gateway of the castle, and it is you, Sir Roland, being one of the youngest, whom I have chosen for this."

At these words Sir Roland was so disappointed that he bit his lip, and closed his helmet over his face so that the other knights might not see it. For a moment he felt as if he must reply angrily to the commander, and tell him that it was not right to leave so sturdy a knight behind when he was eager to fight. But he struggled against his feeling and went quietly to look after his duties at the gate. The gateway was high and narrow, and was reached from outside by a high, narrow bridge that crossed the moat, which surrounded the castle on every side. When an enemy approached, the knight on guard rang a great bell just inside the gate, and the bridge was drawn up against the castle wall so that no one could come across the moat. So the giants had long ago given up trying to attack the castle itself.

To-day the battle was to be in the dark hollow in the forest, and it was not likely that there would be anything to do at the castle gate except to watch it like a common doorkeeper. It was not strange that Sir Roland thought some one else might have done this.

Presently all the other knights marched out in their flashing armor, their red plumes waving over their heads, and their spears in their hands. The lord of the castle stopped only to tell Sir Roland to keep guard over the gate until they all returned, and to let no one enter. Then they went into the shadows of the forest and were soon lost to sight.

Sir Roland stood looking after them long after they had gone, thinking how happy he would be if he were on the way to battle like them. But after a little he put this out of his mind and tried to think of pleasanter things. It was a long time before anything happened or any word came from the battle.

At last Sir Roland saw one of the knights come limping down the path to the castle, and he went out on the bridge to meet him. Now this knight was not a brave one, and he had been frightened away as soon as he was wounded.

"I have been hurt," he said, "so that I cannot fight any more. But I could watch the gate for you if you would like to go back in my place."

At first Sir Roland's heart leaped with joy at this, but then he remembered what the commander had told him on going away, and he said:

"I should like to go, but a knight belongs where his commander has put him. My place is here at the gate, and I cannot open it even for you. Your place is at the battle."

The knight was ashamed when he heard this, and he presently turned about and went into the forest again.

So Sir Roland kept guard silently for another hour. Then there came an old beggar woman down the path to the castle and asked Sir Roland if she might come in and have some food. He told her that no one could enter the castle that day, but that he would send a servant out to her with food, and that she might sit and rest as long as she would.

"I have been past the hollow in the forest where the battle is going on," said the old woman, while she was waiting for her food.

"And how do you think it is going?" asked Sir Roland.

"Badly for the knights, I am afraid," said the old woman. "The giants are fighting as they have never fought before. I should think you had better go and help your friends."

"I should like to, indeed," said Sir Roland. "But I am set to guard the gateway of the castle, and cannot leave."

"One fresh knight would make a great difference when they are all weary with fighting," said the old woman. "I should think that, while there are no enemies about, you would be much more useful there."

"You may well think so," said Sir Roland, "and so may I; but it is neither you nor I that is commander here."

"I suppose," said the old woman, "that you are one of the kind of knights who like to keep out of fighting. You are lucky to have so good an excuse for staying at home." And she laughed a thin and taunting laugh.

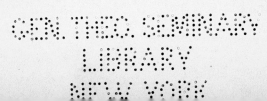

Then Sir Roland was very angry and thought that if it were only a man instead of a woman he would show him whether he liked fighting or no. But as it was a woman he shut his lips and set his teeth hard together, and as the servant came just then with the food he had sent for he gave it to the old woman quickly, and shut the gate that she might not talk to him any more.

It was not very long before he heard some one calling outside. Sir Roland opened the gate, and saw standing at the other end of the drawbridge a little old man in a long black cloak. "Why are you knocking here?" he said. "The castle is closed to-day."

"Are you Sir Roland?" said the little old man.

"Yes," said Sir Roland.

"Then you ought not to be staying here when your commander and his knights are having so hard a struggle with the giants, and when you have the chance to make of yourself the greatest knight in this kingdom. Listen to me! I have brought you a magic sword."

As he said this, the old man drew from under his coat a wonderful sword that flashed in the sunlight as if it were covered with diamonds. "This is the sword of all swords," he said, "and it is for you, if you will leave your idling here by the castle gate and carry it to the battle. Nothing can stand before it. When you lift it the giants will fall back, your master will be saved, and you will be crowned the victorious knight—the one who will soon take his commander's place as lord of the castle."

Now Sir Roland believed that it was a magician who was speaking to him, for it certainly appeared

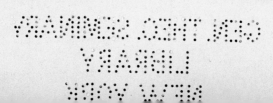

to be a magic sword. It seemed so wonderful that the sword should be brought to him that he reached out his hand as though he would take it, and the little old man came forward as though he would cross the drawbridge into the castle. But as he did so it came to Sir Roland's mind again that the bridge and the gateway had been intrusted to him, and he called out "No!" to the old man, so that he stopped where he was standing. But he waved the shining sword in the air again and said, "It is for you! Take it, and win the victory!"

Sir Roland was really afraid that if he looked any longer at the sword, or listened to any more words of the old man, he would not be able to hold himself within the castle. For this reason he struck the great bell at the gateway, which was the signal for the servants inside to pull in the chains of the drawbridge, and instantly they began to pull and the drawbridge came up, so that the old man could not cross it to enter the castle, nor Sir Roland to go out.

Then, as he looked across the moat, Sir Roland saw a wonderful thing. The little old man threw off his black cloak, and as he did so he began to grow bigger and bigger, until in a minute more he was a giant as tall as any in the forest. At first Sir Roland could scarcely believe his eyes. Then he realized that this must be one of their giant enemies, who had changed himself to a little old man through some magic power that he might make his way into the castle while all the knights were away. Sir Roland shuddered to think what might have happened if he had taken the sword and left the gate unguarded. The giant shook his fist across the moat that lay between them, and then, knowing that he could do nothing more, he went angrily back into the forest.

Sir Roland now resolved not to open the gate again, and to pay attention to no other visitor. But it was not long before he heard a sound that made him spring forward in joy. It was the bugle of the lord of the castle and there came sounding after it the bugles of many of the knights that were with him, pealing so joyfully that Sir Roland was sure they were safe and happy. As they came nearer he could hear their shouts of victory. So he gave the signal to let down the drawbridge again, and went out to meet them. They were dusty and bloodstained and weary, but they had won the battle with the giants; and it had been such a great victory that there had never been a happier homecoming.

Sir Roland greeted them all as they passed in over the bridge, and then, when he had closed the gate and fastened it, he followed them into the great hall of the castle. The lord of the castle took his place on the highest seat, with the other knights about him, and Sir Roland came forward with the key of the gate to give his account of what he had done in the place to which the commander had appointed him. The lord of the castle bowed to him as a sign for him to begin, but just as he opened his mouth to speak, one of the knights cried out:

"The shield! the shield! Sir Roland's shield!"

Every one turned and looked at the shield which Sir Roland carried on his left arm. He himself could see only the top of it, and did not know what they could mean. But what they saw was the golden star of knighthood, shining brightly from the center of Sir Roland's shield. There had never been such amazement in the castle before.

Sir Roland knelt before the lord of the castle to receive his commands. He still did not know why every one was looking at him so excitedly, and wondered if he had in some way done wrong.

"Speak, Sir Knight," said the commander, as soon as he could find his voice after his surprise, "and tell us all that has happened to-day at the castle. Have you been attacked? Have any giants come hither? Did you fight them alone?"

"No, my Lord," said Sir Roland. "Only one giant has been here, and he went away silently when he found he could not enter."

Then he told all that had happened through the day.

When he had finished, the knights all looked at one another, but no one spoke a word. Then they looked again at Sir Roland's shield, to make sure that their eyes had not deceived them, and there the golden star was still shining.

After a little silence the lord of the castle spoke. "Men make mistakes," he said, "but our silver shields are never mistaken. Sir Roland has fought and won the hardest battle of all to-day."

Then the others all rose and saluted Sir Roland, who was the youngest knight that ever carried the golden star.

From *Why the Chimes Rang and Other Stories*, by Raymond MacDonald Alden. Used by permission of the publishers, Bobbs-Merrill Co.

II

THEODORE ROOSEVELT'S FIGHT FOR
STRENGTH

FROM the days of babyhood, Theodore Roosevelt
had been in delicate health. He was a victim of
that dread disease, asthma, but in spite of his constant suffering he had never allowed himself to be
made an invalid. Often his father took him out at
night on long drives in search of a breath of fresh
air, for such was his disease that it often seemed
that he could not even breathe, and that he must
strangle. Whenever he was strong enough he took
an active part in the games of the other children,
and even at the age of eleven he had begun to be
very much interested in animals, plants, and insects.

His father realized that if Theodore was ever to
become a man of great strength he must do everything possible to make his body strong. So Mr.
Roosevelt had one of the rooms of their home turned
into a kind of open-air gymnasium, fully equipped
with every sort of swing, bar, and seesaw. Many
were the happy hours which the Roosevelt children
and their friends spent there. To Theodore, however, those hours were filled with hard work.

The days of Theodore Roosevelt's boyhood sped
by. Several summers were spent on the Hudson
River, another in Germany, where the children
lived in a German family and studied hard on the
difficult German language. They even traveled in
Egypt, sailing on the river Nile. On this trip

Theodore spent long hours hunting and preserving animals and birds for his "Roosevelt Museum."

Yet during all these otherwise happy days, Theodore still suffered frequently from severe attacks of asthma, even though he was a leader in both games and work. In his letters to his father and mother, however, if he referred to his illness at all it was usually without complaint. He wrote to them at great length regarding his hunting, his games, his beloved study of natural history, and of boxing, which was one of his favorite amusements, in spite of the "bloody nose" and "purple eyes" which often resulted.

Never during all these years did he complain, nor did he lessen his struggles to build for himself a strong, well body. We can imagine him, gritting his teeth and throwing back his head, and doggedly saying to himself, "I *will* make my body strong."

His hard work was slowly rewarded, for he kept growing stronger every day. His parents realized how unusual a boy their son Theodore was in the strength and power of his character. They did everything possible to aid him in his struggle for physical health. In the Maine woods he learned, on long hunting trips, how to endure the rigors of that outdoor life, and little by little he won in his long fight against ill health and disease.

It is hard to believe that when Theodore Roosevelt, at the age of eighteen, entered Harvard College, he was the equal, from the physical standpoint, of any man in the university. He was a light-weight boxer and a swift runner, and in every way, mentally and physically, he was ready to take his place in the life of the school.

In 1909, thirty-three years after he entered
Harvard, Theodore Roosevelt set sail again for
Africa. The years since his graduation had been
filled to the brim, with work on his ranch in Dakota,
politics, the Cuban war, and as President of the
United States. Through all those years his fine
bodily vigor had never failed him, and he had often
performed deeds of physical endurance which amazed
his friends.

Who would have dreamed that the delicate boy
of many years ago would one day become a powerful
man? Truly, he had succeeded in making his body
strong.

It is very certain that few other lads ever made a
more determined fight against physical weakness
nor won a more decided victory. He, to a greater
extent than any other American, by his victory
over pain and disease, has shown us what a great
mind and a strong body can accomplish.

III

THE GOLDEN SCEPTER

Now, it came to pass that Ahasuerus, king of the Persians, reigned from India even to Ethiopia. Great was the power of King Ahasuerus and great were his riches. In his palace were white, green, and blue hangings, fastened with cords of fine linen and purple to silver rings and pillars of marble. The beds were of gold and silver upon a pavement of red and blue and white and black marble. The vessels from which the king drank were of gold, and many were the feasts that he gave.

Now, in the palace there was a certain Hebrew, Mordecai, who had been carried away from Jerusalem into captivity. He brought up Esther, his uncle's daughter, for she had neither father nor mother. The maid was fair and beautiful whom Mordecai had taken for his own daughter.

It fell on a day that Esther was brought to the king, and she found favor in his sight and he showed kindness to her. The king loved Esther above all women, so that he set the royal crown upon her head and made her queen.

But the king knew not that Esther was of the Hebrews, the daughter of Mordecai, who sat in the king's gate. It happened that Mordecai learned that two of the king's servants plotted to take the life of the king. Mordecai told Esther, and Esther warned the king thereof in Mordecai's name. The two men were both hanged on a tree and the account was written in the book of chronicles of the king.

After these things did King Ahasuerus promote Haman, the Agagite, and set him above all the princes that were with him. All the king's servants that were in the king's gate bowed and reverenced Haman, for the king had so commanded them. But Mordecai bowed not nor did Haman reverence.

When Haman saw that Mordecai bowed not nor did him reverence, then was Haman full of wrath, and he scorned to lay hands on Mordecai alone, but he planned to destroy all the Hebrews throughout the whole kingdom of Ahasuerus, even the people of Mordecai.

Haman went in to the king and said to him: "There is a certain people scattered abroad in all the provinces of your kingdom. Their laws are different from your laws. Therefore it is not to your profit to suffer them. If it please the king, let it be written that they may be destroyed. I will pay ten thousand talents of silver to the hands of those who have charge of the business."

The king took the ring from his hand and gave it to Haman, the enemy of the Hebrews. He said, "The silver is given to you, the people also, to do with them as it seems good to you."

Then did Haman send letters by posts into all the king's provinces, to destroy, to kill, and to cause to perish all the Hebrews, both young and old, little children and women, in one day, even the thirteenth day of the twelfth month, and to take their spoil as a prey.

When Mordecai saw all that was done, he rent his clothes and put on sackcloth with ashes, and went out into the midst of the city and cried with a loud and bitter cry. And in every province, wherever the king's commandment came, there was great mourning among the Hebrews, and fasting and weeping and wailing; and many lay in sackcloth and ashes.

Esther's maids came and told her of it. Then was the queen exceedingly grieved, and sent word to Mordecai to know what it was and why it was. Mordecai told all that had happened to him and of the king's decree concerning the Hebrews. He sent word again to Esther that she should go in to the king to make a request before him for her people.

Esther replied to Mordecai saying, "All the king's servants and the people of the king's provinces, do know, that whoever, whether man or woman, shall come unto the king who is not called, there is a law to put him to death, except the king shall hold out the golden scepter that he may live. I have not been called to come to the king these thirty days."

Then Mordecai answered Esther: "Think not that you shall escape in the king's house more than all the Hebrews, for if you altogether hold your peace at this time, then shall deliverance arise for the Hebrews from another place, but you and your father's house shall be destroyed. Who knows whether you are come to the kingdom for such a time as this?"

Esther sent Mordecai this answer, "Go, gather together all the Hebrews and fast you for me, and neither eat nor drink three days, night or day. I also and my maidens will fast likewise, and so will I go in to the king. If I perish, I perish."

So Mordecai went his way and did according to

all that Esther had commanded him. Now, it came to pass on the third day that Esther put on her royal apparel and stood in the inner court of the king's house, and the king sat on his royal throne.

When the king saw Esther the queen standing in the court, she obtained favor in his sight and he held out to her the golden scepter that was in his hand. Esther drew near and touched the top of the scepter.

Then the king said to her: "What will you, Queen Esther? What is your request? It shall be given you even to the half of my kingdom."

Esther answered, "If it seem good to the king, let the king and Haman come this day to the banquet that I have prepared for him."

Then the king said, "Cause Haman to make haste that he may do as Esther has said." So the king and Haman came to the banquet which Esther had prepared.

The king said to Esther at the banquet: "What is your petition and it shall be granted you? What is your request? Even to the half of my kingdom it shall be performed."

Esther answered, "If I have found favor in the sight of the king, and if it please the king to grant my petition and to perform my request, let the king and Haman come again to-morrow to the banquet that I shall prepare for them."

Then went Haman forth that day joyful and with a glad heart; but when Haman saw that Mordecai, the Hebrew in the king's gate, stood not up nor moved for him, he was full of indignation against Mordecai.

Haman told his wife and his friends of all his good fortune, saying, "Esther the queen let no man come in to the banquet that she had prepared but the king and myself; and to-morrow am I invited to her also with the king. Yet all this avails me nothing as long as I see Mordecai the Hebrew sitting at the king's gate."

Then said Haman's wife and friends to him, "Let a gallows be made fifty cubits high and to-morrow speak to the king that Mordecai be hanged thereon. Then go you in merrily with the king to the banquet." The saying pleased Haman well and he caused the gallows to be made.

On that night the king could not sleep and he commanded the book of records to be brought and they were read to the king. It was found written therein that Mordecai had told of two of the king's servants who had sought to kill him. And the king said, "What honor and dignity has been done to Mordecai for this?"

The king's servants said to him, "There has nothing been done to Mordecai for this."

And the king said, "Who is in the court?" Now Haman was come into the court to ask the king to hang Mordecai on the gallows that he had prepared.

The king's servants said to him, "Behold, Haman stands in the court."

The king said, "Let him come in." So Haman came in.

The king said to him, "What shall be done to the man whom the king delights to honor?" Now Haman thought in his heart, "Who would the king delight to honor more than myself?"

And Haman answered the king, "For the man whom the king delights to honor, let the king's apparel be brought which the king wears and the horse that the king rides on and the crown royal which is set on his head. And let this apparel and horse be delivered to one of the king's most noble princes that they may array the man whom the king delights to honor and bring him on horseback through the streets of the city and proclaim before him, 'Thus shall it be done to the man whom the king delights to honor.'"

Then the king said to Haman, "Make haste and take the apparel and the horse as you have said, and do even so to Mordecai the Hebrew that sits at the king's gate; let nothing fail of all that you have spoken."

Then took Haman the apparel and the horse, and arrayed Mordecai and brought him on horseback through the streets of the city, and proclaimed before him, "Thus shall be done to the man whom the king delights to honor." And Mordecai came again to the king's gate, but Haman hastened to his house mourning.

Haman told his friends and his wife all that had befallen him. Then said the wise men and his wife to him, "If Mordecai be of the Hebrews before whom you have begun to fall, you shall not prevail against him, but shall surely fall before him."

While they were yet talking the king's servants came to bring Haman to the banquet that Esther had prepared. So the king and Haman came to the banquet with Esther the queen.

And the king said again to Esther: "What is

your petition, Queen Esther? It shall be granted you. What is your request? It shall be performed even to the half of my kingdom."

Then Esther the queen said, "If I have found favor in your sight, O king, and if it please the king, let my life be given at my petition and the lives of my people at my request, for we are sold, I and my people, to be destroyed, to be slain, and to perish."

King Ahasuerus answered Esther the queen, "Who is he and where is he that does presume in his heart to do so?"

Esther said, "The enemy is this wicked Haman." Then Haman was afraid before the king and queen.

One of the servants said to the king, "Behold, the gallows fifty cubits high which Haman has made for Mordecai!"

The king said, "Hang Haman thereon." So they hanged Haman on the gallows which he had prepared for Mordecai. Then was the king's wrath pacified.

On that day did the king give the house of Haman to Esther, the queen. Mordecai came before the king because Esther had told what he was to her. The king took off his ring which he had taken from Haman and gave it to Mordecai. Esther set Mordecai over the house of Haman.

Esther spoke yet again to the king and fell down at his feet and besought him with tears to put away the mischief of Haman against the Hebrews. The king held out his golden scepter to Esther: so Esther rose and stood before the king and said, "If it please the king and I have found favor in his sight, let it be written to reverse the letters devised by

Haman to destroy the Hebrews that are in the king's provinces. How can I endure to see the evil that shall come upon my people or how can I endure to see the destruction of my kindred?"

Then King Ahasuerus said to Esther and to Mordecai, "Behold, I have given Esther the house of Haman, and him they have hanged on the gallows because he laid his hands upon the Hebrews. Write you also for the Hebrews, as you like, in the king's name and seal it with the king's ring, for the writing which is written in the king's name and sealed with the king's ring, may no man reverse."

And Mordecai wrote in the king's name and sealed it with the king's ring, and sent letters by posts on horseback, and riders on mules, camels, and young dromedaries.

Mordecai went out from the presence of the king in royal apparel of blue and white and with a great crown of gold and with a garment of fine linen and purple. The Hebrews had light and gladness, and joy and honor.

From *The Bible in Graded Story*, Vol. III, by Clara Belle Baker and Edna Dean Baker. The Abingdon Press. Used by permission.

IV

THE BOY WHO WAS NOT AFRAID

SENG had attended the mission school from the time he was a little boy in the kindergarten until the time of the Boxer War. His mother and father were Christians and Seng had no thoughts of being anything else himself.

"The Boxers are fighting the Christians wherever they can find them," his father said to him one day. That was when Seng was ten years old.

"And who are the Boxers?" asked Seng.

"They are some of our own people who are making war against the foreigners and the Christians," replied his father. "They think the foreigners come here to do us harm instead of good. They are determined that not one of them shall remain in China."

"But where will the missionaries go? Will they return to their own country?"

"They will not have the chance, son," said Seng's father sadly. "The Boxers are cruel. The Christians can escape upon the promise that they will worship the gods; without that promise they are killed."

"We, too?" gasped Seng.

"It may be," replied the father.

"But if one should just pretend to worship the idols, would they let him go if he really was a Christian?" Seng asked again.

"Seng," said his father quietly, "Christians do

not lie. They do not need to be afraid of anything that men can do to them because it is better to do right than be safe."

Seng thought about his father's words many times in the next few days. However, nothing was heard of any trouble in their village and Seng thought that they were to escape.

One day without warning the Boxers came. From house to house they ran as they seized Christians in the village. Seng heard the noise and knew without being told what it all meant.

"Will they take us, father?" he asked.

"Probably they will, son, but you do not need to be afraid." He had scarcely finished speaking when the door burst open, the Boxers entered, and Seng saw his father and mother taken away.

They did not take Seng at first. They thought he was a bright-looking boy and would make a good soldier after a while. One of the men looked straight at him and said, "You will have to come, too, unless you worship the idols."

"I do not," said Seng. "I am a Christian."

"Then you will be punished as they are. Come along."

Just then a tall, important-looking man came along. "What is this?" he asked.

"Only a stubborn lad who insists that he is a Christian," he was told.

The officer turned to Seng.

"Don't you know that you will be punished if you say that?"

"But it is the truth," said Seng.

"You may be killed for saying it," replied the man.

"But it is the truth, anyway," was the answer.
"And if I should order you to be killed right away?"

"My father said that Christians don't need to be afraid," said the boy.

Then the officer said to the Boxer, "Leave him to me," and taking Seng by the arm, he walked away with him. Seng was terribly frightened. At last they entered a great house where everything was much finer than anything Seng had ever seen. The man looked straight at him again. "I shall come back soon for you. Will you stay here?"

Seng was more frightened than he had ever been in all his life, but he said, "Yes, I'll stay." Probably the man had gone to bring soldiers to kill him right there; perhaps something more dreadful than he had ever heard of was about to happen. The door was not fastened and he thought of trying to run away, but he remembered his father's saying, "Christians do not need to be afraid," and he knew that it would not be honest to run away. It seemed a very long time before the officer returned and he was still alone.

"Why didn't you try to get away?" the man asked.

"I said I should stay," was the answer from Seng and the man looked at him curiously. He had left the door unfastened on purpose to see if Seng would not try to escape.

"Well, I have decided that if you will worship idols, as I do, I will let you stay here in my house where you will be taken care of as if you were my boy; otherwise—well, you know what happens to Christians?"

"Yes, I know, but I am a Christian and I always will be."

The man was angry. This was an unusual sort of boy. Never had he seen another like him. He should have one more chance. At last he said:

"Yes, you are now, but perhaps after a while you will do as I want you to."

Seng thought hard for a minute. Then he thought of his father and he did not even feel afraid as he replied firmly:

"No, Christians never change, I couldn't."

It seemed hours before the man spoke at last.

"Seng, you are a strange boy, a brave boy. You are to stay with me here, even if you are a Christian, now and always."

Everyland.   Used by permission of the publishers.

V

THE GREAT STONE FACE

ONE afternoon when the sun was going down, a mother and her little boy sat at the door of their cottage talking about the Great Stone Face. Now the Great Stone Face was a gigantic face against the mountain side, sculptured there by nature when the mountains were being made. It was so large that the arch of the forehead was a hundred feet in height. The nose was equally long, and the vast lips, could they have spoken, would have rolled their thunder tones across the valley.

This giant face was full of kindness and affection. It had a smile that seemed to come from a vast, warm heart, full of friendliness and love for every person.

"Mother," said the boy Ernest, "I wish that the Old Man of the Mountain could speak, for he looks so kind that his voice must needs be pleasant. If I were to see a man with such a face I am sure I should love him dearly."

"If an old prophecy should come to pass," answered his mother, "we may see a man some time or other, with exactly such a face as that." And then his mother told him a legend which for many years had been handed down from generation to generation by the people of the valley. The story was that at some future day a child should be born in this valley who was to become the greatest and noblest man of his time, and whose countenance should bear an exact resemblance to the Great Stone Face. This man was to come and live in the valley and be the ruler of its people.

"O Mother! Mother!" cried Ernest, clapping his hands. "I do hope that I shall live to see this great and good man."

Ernest never forgot the story that his mother told him. He always thought of it when in the evening he would sit in the door of his log-cottage home, looking out upon the Great Stone Face, lighted up by the setting sun. Many times did Ernest think of the story his mother had told about the coming of the great man. For hours Ernest would look upon the face, and imagine it to be the features of this great personage who was to come and rule over the valley.

One day there came a rumor that startled the people of the valley. It was reported that a great man who had been born in the valley, and who when a youth had left it to seek his fortune in other lands, was returning and that he was the great and wise man who was to come to them. This man's name was Gathergold, and he was to arrive at sunset on a certain day to take possession of a splendid mansion that had been built for him.

The evening had come, and a large group of people were assembled to welcome the great Mr. Gathergold. The rumbling of wheels was heard, and there arose a cry, "Here he comes! Here comes the great Mr. Gathergold!"

Ernest, full of excitement, shouted with the rest to welcome the coming wise man; but when Mr. Gathergold stepped from his carriage, and Ernest saw a wrinkled, cruel, and shrewd face, he was much disappointed. He turned toward the Great Stone Face, now gilded by the last sunbeams, and then he knew that Mr. Gathergold was not the great man who was to come to the valley. As Ernest stood gazing upon the Great Stone Face, the kindly lips seemed to say, "He will come. Fear not, Ernest, the man will come."

The years went on. Ernest had grown to be a man. By this time poor Mr. Gathergold was dead and buried, and perhaps forgotten.

It so happened that a native son of the valley, many years before, had enlisted as a soldier, and, after a great deal of hard fighting, had become an illustrious commander. He was known in camps and on the battlefield as "Old Blood and Thunder."

This war-worn veteran, now infirm with age, and weary of a military life, had lately declared his purpose of returning to his native valley, there to spend the remainder of his days in quiet and rest.

The inhabitants, his old neighbors and their grown-up children, resolved to welcome the renowned warrior with a salute of cannon and a public dinner, the more so because it was rumored that the likeness of the Great Stone Face had actually appeared in the person of General Blood and Thunder.

When Ernest came with the rest to the festival, he heard the people exclaiming, "'Tis the very same face. Why, it is Old Blood and Thunder himself!" And then the crowd gave a great shout, that went reverberating for miles among the mountains.

Ernest looked upon the Great Stone Face, and then upon the features of General Blood and Thunder. In the old general's visage, Ernest saw the look of stern command, but nothing of kindness, love, and gentleness.

"This is not the man of prophecy," sighed Ernest to himself as he made his way out of the throng, "and the world must wait still longer for the coming man."

More years sped swiftly away. Ernest still dwelt in his native valley, and had now become a man of middle age. By degrees he had come to be known and loved by many people, for he had given many hours of his life to helping others, and not a day passed but that the world was better because he had lived in it.

When the people's minds had had time to cool a little, they were ready to acknowledge their mistake in imagining General Blood and Thunder to resemble the kindly face on the mountain side.

Then there came a day when it was reported that the great man had surely come, this time as a great statesman. He, like Mr. Gathergold and old Blood and Thunder, was a native of the valley; but he had left it in his early days and taken up the trade of politics. He had been elected to high office and had become celebrated throughout the land.

Many of his admirers thought they had discovered a resemblance between him and the Great Stone Face. So much struck by this likeness were they, indeed, that throughout the country this distinguished gentleman was known by the name of "Old Stony Phiz."

When it was known that Old Stony Phiz was returning to the valley, magnificent preparations were made to receive him. Among the company assembled to do him honor was Ernest, who was still hoping to see the great and wise man come to rule over the valley.

"Hurrah for the great man! Hurrah for Old Stony Phiz!" echoed the cry as he approached.

"Here he is now!" cried those who stood nearest to Ernest. "There! There! Look at Old Stony Phiz and then at the Old Man of the Mountain, and see if they are not as like as twin brothers!"

"Is he not the very picture of your Old Man of the Mountain?" said Ernest's neighbor, turning to him.

"No," said Ernest bluntly, "I see little or no likeness," and again Ernest turned away disappointed.

As Ernest turned to look upon the Great Stone Face, he seemed to hear a voice saying, "Lo, here I am, Ernest. I have waited longer than thou and am not yet weary. Fear not, the man will yet come."

Now while the years were passing there had come a poet to the earth. The songs of this poet had found their way to Ernest, who was now growing old. He read the beautiful poems each evening after he had finished his toil, as he sat upon the bench before his cottage door. At intervals he would look upon the Great Stone Face, and his soul thrilled within him. "Majestic friend," he murmured, addressing the Great Stone Face, "is not this poet worthy to resemble thee?" The Face on the mountain side seemed to smile but answered not a word.

It came to pass that on a summer day the poet came to visit the valley. Even before he had reached the valley, he heard of Ernest and his many deeds of kindness and helpfulness to friends and neighbors. He resolved, therefore, to visit Ernest, and upon his arrival inquired at once where Ernest dwelt.

Approaching the door, he there found the now venerable Ernest, holding in his hand a volume of poems, which at times he read, and then with a finger between the leaves, looked lovingly at the Great Stone Face.

The poet sat on the bench beside him, and he and Ernest talked together. As Ernest listened to the poet, he imagined that the Great Stone Face was bending forward to listen too.

While they talked together, the poet noticed a sad look upon Ernest's face. "Wherefore are you sad?" inquired the poet.

"Because," replied Ernest, "all through my life I have awaited the fulfillment of a prophecy, and when I read these poems I hoped that it might be fulfilled in you, and that you might be the great man who was to come to our valley."

"Once more you must be disappointed," answered the poet, "for I am not worthy to represent the man typified by yonder face on the mountain side."

"And why?" asked Ernest, as he pointed to the volume. "These words are beautiful and the thoughts are true."

"Alas," said the poet, "but my life has not matched my thoughts and my words." The poet spoke sadly and his eyes were dimmed with tears. So likewise were those of Ernest.

Now it had long been the custom of Ernest, at the hour of sunset, to address his friends and neighbors as they assembled on the hillside in the open air. He and the poet, arm in arm, still talking together as they went, now proceeded to the spot. Ernest took his place among the rocks which made for him a natural pulpit. He began to speak, giving to the people what was in his heart and mind.

The poet, as he listened, felt that the life and character of Ernest were more beautiful than any poetry he had ever written. His eyes were bright with tears as he gazed reverently upon Ernest's face. He said within himself, "Surely here is a prophet and a sage."

At that moment, as Ernest was about to utter some beautiful thoughts, his face took on a sudden grandeur of expression. The poet, looking from Ernest to the Great Stone Face on the mountain side, was suddenly struck by the resemblance between the two.

"Behold! Behold!" he cried, throwing his arms aloft, "Ernest is himself the likeness of the Great Stone Face."

Then all the people looked, and saw that what the poet said was true. The prophecy was fulfilled. The great man had come to the valley. Ernest himself, by his good deeds and kindly life, had become the great man of the valley.

Adapted from the story by NATHANIEL HAWTHORNE.

VI

THE BOY WHO GAVE A CUP OF
COLD WATER

In the northern quarter of the village of Nazareth stood the humble home of Joseph the carpenter. Fragrant vines clambered over its rough stone walls and touched the flat roof, while palms stood as sentinels to guard against the heat of the noonday sun.

At the rear of the home was a room used by Joseph as a shop. Here on the afternoon of a summer day he and the youthful Jesus worked busily, hewing and smoothing a timber to be used in the repair of a house on the opposite side of the village. When they had finished the task the boy stood for a moment gazing away over the jagged purple hills which, to the westward, half encircled the village nestling at their feet.

"Come, son," said Joseph, "we must hasten if we would complete our work on Neighbor Benjamin's house, for the shadows are already beginning to lengthen."

Grasping the finished timber, the sturdy youth swung it lightly to his shoulder. Joseph gathered up the needed tools, and with this they moved briskly down the narrow street until they came to the house where they were mending the roof.

The timber was soon made fast, and they began to replace the tiles which had been removed.

Suddenly the boy, whose ears were keener than those of Joseph, paused. "Listen!" he said. "Did you hear a trumpet sound! And now the tramp of horses' feet? See! The people are running out from their houses. They are hastening toward the village well. What can be the matter? Shall we not go?"

"It is strange," answered Joseph in his quiet voice. "Let us see this last tile in place and then we too will pass by the well and learn what strange visitors have honored our village with their presence."

Quickly their work was finished, and Joseph, with Jesus at his side, set out for the well, where now they could see a large crowd of people gathered.

As they approached the place they took in the scene. A band of soldiers, armed with spears and wearing the helmets of the Romans, had arrived at the well and were quenching their thirst from its sparkling depths.

The haughty Roman soldiers gave little attention to the villagers, who encircled their group at the well. Having satisfied their own thirst, they turned to the comfort of their tired horses. Water was drawn and the animals eagerly drank great draughts from the stone trough which stood by the edge of the well.

During this interval none of the soldiers had noticed or even given a glance toward a figure who had immediately become the center of interest to the people of the village. This was a man perhaps forty years of age, who was a prisoner of the Roman band. Around his neck was riveted a collar of brass. To this a thong was tied, the other end of which was attached to the saddle of one of the horses. The prisoner's hands were bound behind him. His scanty clothing was in shreds. His dark hair was matted with dust and clogged with blood which oozed from a wound on his head. His feet were bare and were bleeding from the sharp rocks over which he had been forced at a rapid pace by his heartless captors. Weary to the point of exhaustion, and suffering from thirst and the pain of his wounds, the prisoner had sunk to the ground in a stupor as soon as the band came to a halt.

"Who is he?" "What has he done?" "Will they not give him water to drink?" were the whispers that ran around the pitying crowd. But none dared brave the haughty stare of the leader, as with contemptuous eyes he swept the circle about him.

While the excitement was at its height an aged rabbi stepped forth from the crowd and gravely saluted the one in command. "Your prisoner— has he committed a serious crime?" inquired the rabbi.

"Serious enough," said the leader. "He has escaped from the galleys to which he was sentenced for life."

"But his crime?" pursued the rabbi.

"That of plotting against the life of a Roman citizen," sternly replied his captor.

Upon these words the pity of the crowd for the prisoner froze. A criminal!

"So he would take the life of another!" said one.

"Has he forgotten the command of Jehovah, 'Thou shalt not kill'?" spoke a second.

"Let the wretch take his punishment then," muttered a third. None spoke in kindness, nor did any offer the prisoner help or service.

During this interval he had lain weak and almost insensible in the dust. His breath came in sobbing sighs, and a deep pallor had spread over his face. He expected no mercy and asked for none.

Then there was a little stir in the crowd. It parted at the edge and a young boy stepped from the circle. Speaking to no one, he took up a pitcher of water from the curb of the well and approached the prisoner. Unmindful of the hostile eyes of the soldiers, he lifted the head of the prisoner and put the water to his lips. "Drink ye of this," he said in a quiet voice. Eagerly the exhausted man quaffed the refreshing water, gratitude shining from his eyes. Then, placing his hand on the prisoner's head, the boy spoke a simple prayer: "The God of our fathers bless and keep thee!"

"Amen!" responded the group.

His errand of mercy completed, the boy passed out through the crowd, which opened to make way for him. Jesus of Nazareth had given a cup of cold water to one of the least of his brethren.

From *The Rules of the Game*, by Floyd W. Lambertson. The Abingdon Press. Used by permission.

VII

NOT WHAT WE GIVE, BUT WHAT WE SHARE
(From "THE VISION OF SIR LAUNFAL")

Sir Launfal was one of the youngest of the knights, but he was very strong. He was rich, too. He had more money than he knew what to do with. He lived in a castle and had everything he wanted. Sometimes he threw a piece of money to a beggar, and when he heard that people were poor he sent them a piece of gold. But he never went to see them, and he was so rich that he might have given away more than he did without knowing the difference. As for his castle, it was beautiful inside with many splendid rooms, but no one ever saw them except Sir Launfal's friends, who were as rich as he was and did not care much for the beauty of the castle because they saw others like it so often.

Sir Launfal, like the other knights, decided that he would go on a long journey and search for the Holy Grail. It was early summer, a good time to travel, and he planned to put on his best armor and ride on his favorite horse and to start the very next morning.

That night he had a dream.

In his dream he rode out of the castle with golden spurs on his heels and armor that gleamed like gold. He felt strong and happy. The birds sang as if their throats would burst. The leaves on the trees were green and rustling. Only his own castle looked cold and stern, as if it waited impatiently for winter.

He was glad to be out of it, riding away to find the Grail.

Just then, a beggar, clothed in dirty rags, lifted his hand and begged for help.

Sir Launfal was disgusted. The beggar was so dirty and thin! What business had he to be there at all on such a beautiful day? And he was keeping Sir Launfal from riding on his journey.

The knight looked at him scornfully. Then he put his hand in his pocket and flung him a piece of gold.

The gold fell in the dust, while the beggar straightened his thin shoulders and looked the astonished Sir Launfal in the eye.

"No," he said, "you gave me that gold because you thought you ought to do it, not because you care how ill I am, or how hungry. I would rather have a poor man give me a crust; I would rather have a poor man kind to me and not give me anything at all, than take gold from you who are not kind."

As the beggar spoke, Sir Launfal shivered. He grew colder and colder. The beggar vanished. The birds stopped singing. The leaves withered and fell from the trees, and as Sir Launfal looked about him he saw that it was winter. The ground was covered with snow and ice. He himself was changed. His horse was gone and his splendid armor and golden spurs. He was old; his gray beard helped to keep warm his hollow chest. He was tired; he sat down to rest beside a frozen brook. He was poor; it seemed to him that he had made his long journey searching for the Grail and had not found it, that he had been gone so long that another knight had taken his place in the castle. And now he was so changed that no one knew him; he had been turned away from his own door. Now, indeed, he knew what it meant to be hungry and ill and lonely, like the beggar to whom he had scornfully flung a piece of gold.

As he sat shivering in his ragged clothing, he tried to keep warm by thinking of the hot countries through which he had traveled on his search for the Holy Grail. The best to think of was a burning desert. He had almost forgotten how wretched he was, when he was startled by a voice asking for help.

It was the beggar again!

Sir Launfal did not stop to think how dirty the beggar was—he only thought that he must be as cold and hungry as himself. He divided the moldy crust of bread which was all he had left, and breaking the ice at the edge of the brook, gave the beggar a drink of cold water in the name of Jesus. For he remembered that Jesus gave to the poor.

It grew light suddenly, and the beggar became very beautiful, as if it were Jesus himself. And a voice said:

"All these years you have searched for the Holy Grail and have not found it; but the cup which you filled at the brook, from which we drank together, is just as holy.

"'The Holy Supper is kept indeed,
In whatso we share with another's need;
Not what we give, but what we share,
For the gift without the giver is bare;
Who gives himself with his alms feeds three,
Himself, his hungering neighbor, and me.'"

Sir Launfal awoke with a start. Yes, he was still young and strong. He was lying in his own castle. The warm air of summer came in through the window. It had been a dream. But he could not forget it. He had seen a beggar become Jesus, who had spoken to him and told him that the Holy Grail was not nearly so important as sharing what he had with those who needed it. So Sir Launfal hung up his armor and opened his castle gates, and if you had gone by in those days you would not have thought that the castle looked at all stern, because the doors were wide open. People who had poor homes went in and enjoyed the beautiful rooms as they had never been enjoyed before, and Sir Launfal was always there to receive them as he would his own friends. And when he heard other knights talking of the Holy Grail, and how they were intending to spend their lives hunting for it, he thought of his dream and said nothing at all.

From the poem by JAMES RUSSELL LOWELL, "The Vision of Sir Launfal," adapted by FRANCES M. DADMUN in "Living Together." Used by permission of the publishers, The Beacon Press.

VIII

HOW MIRZA KHAN TOLD THE TRUTH

In Pawlgaun, not far from Siliguri, lived Mirza Khan with his father and mother, his brothers and sisters. Mirza Khan had been helping the others plant paddy all day, except during the two hours at noon when the great fierce sun beat down and made it impossible to work. Weary with splashing around in the mud he was glad when late in the afternoon his father said, "Mirza, go to the tank and drive in the buffalo."

His father was poor and owned only one buffalo. It was Mirza's task to look after this when it was not being used, and early that morning he had taken it to the tank for the day. He liked nothing better than to drive this great, ungainly beast, and when he went to pasture he always went as far as he dared.

"Accha!" he cried eagerly when he heard his father's command, hastily thrust his last bunch of rice roots into the mud, washed the soil from his hands, and ran out to the road to bring the buffalo.

He had driven the buffalo out of the tank, leaped on its back, and started home swinging his legs against the bulky sides when a meettaiwala met him.

"Hello!" cried Mirza. "How many jelabis for a pice?"

"Two," replied the meettaiwala.

"You are not selling to a raja; we always get

three for a pice here," answered Mirza, preparing to drive on.

"But, my jelabis are very good," pleaded the meettaiwala.

"So are Mussufur Jung's," retorted Mirza. "He comes almost every day, and everybody likes his."

"What is your name?" inquired the meettaiwala.

"Mirza Khan. My father is waiting for me at Pawlgaun. I must go. Give me three jelabis for a pice."

"Accha! I will give you three jelabis for nothing, if you will take a message for me to Balipore."

"Balipore is a mile from here. Make it five and I will go."

"No, I will give you four."

"Accha! Wait till I drive the buffalo back to the tank."

Mirza soon returned. "Find Mohommed Ali, the sampwala, and tell him there is a fair to-morrow at Chandpore," said the meettaiwala, and held out four jelabis.

Mirza took the four jelabis and ran as fast as he could over the fields to Balipore. He had no difficulty to find the sampwala, for he was performing in an open place near the well and all the village was gathered about him. He was in the midst of a wonderful trick. He was actually pulling whole rupees out of the ears and noses of the bystanders. They were real rupees, for he sounded each one on a stone as soon as he plucked it out.

Of course, Mirza could not think of interrupting the sampwala till he was finished. But no sooner had he ended extracting rupees out of the heads of the bystanders than his servant began to dance wildly about the open space playing a gourd and making most comical faces while his master prepared for some new trick. This time he made a plant grow out of a kuje right before their eyes. When this was performed there were other wonders in quick succession. Mirza stood with wide eyes and open mouth, carried away by the man's great power, and forgot all about the buffalo.

At last the magician began to pack up and the people to disperse. Then Mirza first of all remembered his message, and going up hurriedly to the great man he whispered, "There's to be a fair in Chandpore to-morrow."

Mohommed Ali looked hastily up and smiled kindly on Mirza. "Who sent you?" he asked.

"A meettaiwala," replied Mirza.

"Accha! Here is a piece of sugar cane for you," said the magician, handing him a large thick piece.

Mirza eagerly grasped the sugar cane, then all at once he thought of the buffalo. The sun had set. It would be dark in a few moments. What should he do? Greatly frightened, he made a hasty salaam to Ali and rushed back to the tank as fast as his legs would carry him.

It was dark when he reached the tank, but the stars were shining brightly, and the new moon was slowly climbing up the sky. But in the tank not a buffalo was to be seen. For a moment Mirza's heart sank. Had someone stolen the buffalo? Then a more pleasant thought occurred to him. The buffalo knew his way home and had gone off without him.

But now a new terror seized him. What should he tell his father when he finally returned home without the buffalo, especially if the buffalo had gotten there first. "Tell him," whispered a voice in his ear, "tell him you lost your pice, and it took you a long time to find it."

"It is wrong to tell a lie," whispered another voice quietly.

"But I can tell you something better," whispered the first voice. "Tell him a wolf chased you all the way to Balipore."

"Jesus would not tell a lie," whispered the second voice, quietly again.

"I can tell you something better still," whispered the first voice. "Say you heard a leopard and climbed a tree till he had gone away."

"But only a coward will tell a lie," answered the second voice.

"You will be punished if you tell the truth," said the first voice.

"You cannot be brave and manly if you tell a lie," said the second.

So the two voices kept answering back and forth all the way home.

At last Mirza reached the village and stood at the door of his home. "Where have you been?" asked his father sternly. "The buffalo came home alone. Mother has been frightened almost to death and has been weeping for an hour. I have been all the way to the tank and back. Your brothers are searching for you out over the fields now. Where have you been?"

Then Mirza was very sorry for all the trouble he had caused, and big tears began running down his cheeks. "Father," said he, "I'm sorry I have made everybody so unhappy. It was very wrong of me. I met a meettaiwala on the road and he offered me four jelabis to take a message to Balipore. I thought it would take only a little while, but when I saw the sampwala doing wonderful tricks I forgot everything else."

"Mirza, I am glad you told the truth, but you shall not take the buffalo to the tank again for a whole month," answered his father.

This was very severe punishment, indeed, for Mirza. He would rather have had a whipping. But that night when he went to bed he felt braver and stronger than he had ever felt in all his life, for he had learned to tell the truth.

By John W. Simmons.

IX

THE LEGEND OF SAINT CHRISTOPHER

THERE once lived in a far-away land a great giant, Offero by name. It was said that he could swim through mighty torrents, that he could pull forest trees up by their roots, that he could travel for miles through burning sands or over snow-covered mountains, and not grow weary.

One day the mighty Offero left his home and started out in search of one whom he might serve. "For," said he, "I want for my Master the mightiest man in all the world."

He traveled for days until finally he came to a walled city, where he had heard there ruled a great king. When the monarch saw the giant approaching he greeted him gladly, for he saw his strong shoulders and his mighty arms, and he knew that he would be a faithful servant.

"I will make you a leader in my army," said the king. "Go forth and fight my enemies and win great victories for your Master."

Offero fought hard and overcame the enemies of the king. When he returned to the palace he received great glory and honor. As he came into the presence of the king, the mighty monarch arose and said, "You have fought well, Offero. I shall make you the head of my armies, for with you in command I shall never fear any foe."

"Not even Satan?" asked a courtier standing by. But at the mention of Satan, the monarch's face grew pale for he feared Satan above all other foes.

"Why do you fear Satan, O king?" asked Offero. "Is he mightier than yourself? I will leave you, then, for I would serve the strongest Master in the world." Soon Offero left the presence of the king and was on his way in search of Satan, that he might serve him.

Almost before he knew it, Offero found the mighty Satan, who was glad to have the great giant for one of his servants. As before, Offero served his master well, traveling far and wide on his evil errands. Satan was greatly pleased at the work of Offero and one day he said, "With you to serve me, O mighty Offero, I no longer fear the Christ."

"The Christ?" cried Offero. "Do you fear the Christ? Why do you fear him? Is he more powerful than yourself?"

"O yes, Offero," answered Satan, "though I have always been his enemy, I have never succeeded in conquering him. I fear him more than the whole world."

"I will leave you then, as I left the mighty monarch," said Offero in disgust to Satan, "for I could not serve a coward. Let me find the Christ, whom even you fear. Him only shall I serve."

Over raging torrents and burning deserts traveled the mighty Offero. In strange lands he wandered for many months and in different cities all over the world he searched for the Christ whom he would serve, but nowhere could he find him.

He had grown weary of his quest, so he decided to build himself a hut beside a raging river, and there he lived, with still a longing in his heart to find the Christ that he might serve him. But he was not idle, nor was his great strength wasted, for he was so strong that he could carry the people on his back, as he swam across the river from one side to the other. He was always ready to help the weary travelers across, no matter how fierce the storm, or how dark the night.

One night as Offero was just about to go to bed, he heard a faint voice outside his window. A terrible storm was raging. The wind was roaring through the trees of the forest and the great waves of the river beat against the shore. "Offero, Offero." Again sounded the voice, this time a little stronger, "Offero, Offero, won't you come and carry me across the river."

Quick as a flash Offero was up and out of his hut, carrying his lantern in his hand, but he could find no one. He searched the bank, and there, to his surprise, he saw a little child, all cold and wet.

Easily he lifted the small figure of the child to his strong shoulder, and with the help of a staff made his way through the rushing water. At first it was easy, but it seemed to Offero as the wind blew harder and as the rain beat against his face, and as the waters churned about his feet, that the child grew heavier and heavier. He thought that he would never reach the other shore. Bravely he fought against the waves, but even then he could hardly gain headway. The child kept growing heavier and heavier, and his arms were so tightly clasped about Offero's neck that he could scarcely breathe. At last he reached the shore and caught hold of the rocks and grass that he might pull himself out of the water. He was so exhausted that he hardly had strength to stand erect on the river's bank and set his burden down. But then he heard a voice saying, "Offero, you have served me well. From now on you shall be called Christophero, which means Christ-bearer, for in serving me you are helping to carry the burdens of the whole world."

And in the place of the little child, Offero saw the shining figure of the Christ, whom he had sought and found in deeds of service.

X

THE WHITTLER OF CREMONA

It was sundown and Maytime, and Cremona was gay in the wealth of green and gold weather. Revelers in fantastic attire went laughing along the promenades, for it was the last day of carnival week, and grave men and women had been transformed into merry-eyed maskers. Instead of a solemn clerk in office or shop there was a jolly shepherd, or perhaps a dryad, while money lenders, who on other days looked stern and forbidding, frisked about as goats or clowns or apes. Yes, it was gay in Cremona, for it was May and carnival time, and they come but once a year.

Down in a narrow, alleylike street that crept, zigzag fashion, toward the Duomo, three boys were standing in the shadows. They wore no masks, not even a scarlet brow shield to show that they had any part in the merriment that was general on the boulevards, and the shabbiness of their clothing told that they were of Cremona's poor. Perhaps they had crept from the bright-robed throng because of their somber attire; perhaps just to talk over a question that seemed important, for two of them were in earnest conversation, while the third stood quietly by, whittling at a pine stick. He was younger than the others, with a sensitive face and big, expressive eyes that were brown and velvety, and his companions called him Tonio.

"But I tell you, Salvator, every minute lost now is like throwing gold away. People are generous at carnival time, and we can get twenty lira to-night as easily as one when the fun is over, for a merry heart makes an open hand."

"Perhaps you are right, Gulio, and I will go. Shall we start now?"

His brother nodded and replied: "Yes, to the piazza, in front of the Duomo, where a crowd is always passing. You sing, and I will play. Do you want to go too, Tonio?"

Antonio looked up from the stick that was be-beginning to take the semblance of a dagger under his knife, and turned his velvet eyes full on Gulio.

"Yes. I'd like to be with you, even if I cannot sing."

The brothers laughed.

"You certainly cannot sing," Gulio remarked. "You can do nothing but whittle, which is a pity, for that never turns a penny your way. But hurry. People are in their merriest mood now."

And laughing voices sounding from the streets told that he was right.

Gulio picked up his violin, and, followed by Salvator and Antonio, led the way through the alley to a street that skirted the Po. Other Cremonese, both old and young, moved in the same direction, for all wanted to be where the fun was at its height, and that was in the great square in front of the Duomo. The brothers chatted as they went along, for the thought of the money the revelers would give had made them light of heart. But Antonio said little. Gulio's remark, that he could do nothing but whittle, was still in his mind, and while he knew it to be true, it made him sad. He loved music, yet could have no part in making it, for he did not own a violin, and when he tried to sing his voice squeaked so that the boys laughed. It was hard to be just a whittler when his companions could play and sing well.

Soon they were in front of the great cathedral, where a throng continually moved by, the brilliancy of the masks and dominoes seeming to vie with the hues nature had spread across the sky. For the sun had dropped like a ball of flame on the broad Lombardian plains beyond the city, and masses of purple and maroon clouds were piled along the horizon. Now and then a sail fluttered like a white-winged bird as a pleasure bark moved up or down the river, and gold-emblazoned standards and rich caparisons on the horses and carriages of great lords added color to the scene. There is a saying that all nature is glad when Cremona makes merry, and the glowing beauty of the evening seemed to prove it true.

Without losing a minute Gulio took his violin from its case, and tuning it with skillful fingers, began the prelude of a Lombardian folk song. Salvator's voice was sweet and lutelike, and as he sang to his brother's accompaniment, several stopped to listen, and dropped coins into the singer's out-stretched hand when he finished.

Antonio kept on with his whittling until it was so dark he could not see to work. Then he sat on the cathedral steps and waited for the boys.

A man walked by. He wore neither mask nor domino, and seemed to care little about the gaiety. But seeing the youthful musicians, he came close to where they stood.

"That is a pretty song, lad," he said as Salvator finished another ballad. "Would you sing it again to please a lonely man's fancy?"

He seemed to hear nothing but the music as the boy did as he asked, and stood with half-closed eyes listening to the fresh young voice that blended sweetly with the soft violin accompaniment. Then, handing Salvator a coin, he went on down the street, without noticing Antonio, who still sat on the steps.

The boy held the coin up in the waning light and gave a cry.

"*Sacre giorno!*"[1] A gold piece! A gold piece for one song."

Gulio looked at him dubiously. But when he examined the coin, he too exclaimed: "Truly a gold piece! But he can well afford it. That is the great Amati."

Antonio came and looked at the money. He had seen very few gold pieces, and thought it wonderful that a man should give so much. Then, turning to Gulio, he asked, "Who is Amati, and why do you call him great?"

Salvator stared in amazement.

"You have not heard of Amati?" he asked.

But before he could answer Gulio interrupted: "Of course not. Antonio is just a whittler. He knows about knives and woods, but little about music. Amati is a violin maker, the greatest in Italy, and very, very rich. Yet men say he cares for nothing in the world but his work."

The brothers were so happy over their good fortune that they were not willing to stay in the street any longer. They wanted to get home with

___
[1] "*Sacre giorno*"—holy day.

the money, and Antonio had no desire to be there alone. It is jolly to watch a throng of merrymakers when one has companions, but not pleasant to be in the midst of gaiety in which you have no part. So he walked with them as far as the bridge across the Po, then went on to his own home and crept to bed. But he did not sleep, for his brain was afire with a thought that had just come into it. He could not sing. He could do nothing but whittle, and here in his own Cremona was a man who with knives and wood made wonderful violins.

Before dawn next day he was up, and eating a piece of bread, took some things he had made with his knife, and crept out of the house while his parents were still sleeping. Somewhere in the city the master violin maker dwelt, and he meant to find his home. It was not hard, for all Cremona knew of the great Amati, and while the matin bells were still ringing Antonio stood at his door.

The servant growled because he disturbed the house so early and scolded him away, so he waited in the street until he was sure it was time for work to begin, when again he rattled the heavy brass knocker. Again the man was about to drive him away, when the master, hearing the hireling's angry tones and the boy's pleading ones, came to the door.

"I have brought these things for you to see," Antonio answered when questioned. "I cut them out with my knife, and want to know if you think I can learn to make violins."

The great man smiled.

"What is your name, lad?"

"Antonio Stradivarius," came the eager reply.

"And why do you want to make violins?"

The boy's face was very earnest as he looked into the master's, and the velvet eyes seemed to grow darker as he spoke.

"Because I love music, and cannot make any. Salvator and Gulio can both sing and play. You heard them last night in the piazza in front of the Duomo and gave them the gold piece. I love music as much as they, but my voice is squeaky. I can do nothing but whittle."

The master laid his hand on Antonio's shoulder.

"Come into the house and you shall try. The song in the heart is all that matters, for there are many ways of making music. Some play violins, some sing, some paint pictures and make statues, while others till the soil and make flowers bloom. Each sings a song, and helps to make music for the world. If you put your best into it, the song you sing with knives and wood will be just as noble as the one Salvator and Gulio sing with voice or violin."

So Antonio Stradivarius, a boy who could not sing, became a pupil of the great Amati. Day after day he toiled in the workshop. Day after day he hewed persistently and patiently, until at last he had a violin. It was not done in a week, nor in a month, for the master taught him many lessons besides those in cutting and shaping and string placing, one of which was that a tiny bit well done each day is what means great achievement by and by. Sometimes he wanted to hurry and work less carefully than his teacher advised, but gradually he learned that patience is worth more than all things else to him who would excel, and when the instrument was finished he felt repaid for the long days of toil, for the master praised it, and that was a wonderful reward.

Years passed, and he worked on and on. His squeaky voice no longer troubled him, for although it had not improved, and Gulio and Salvator were both singers much loved in Cremona, he had learned that Amati's words were true, and that if there is a song in the heart there is always a way of singing it. So he put his best into his work, and his violins became known all over Italy. Musicians said their tone was marvelously sweet and mellow, and wondered how it could be. But to Antonio it seemed very simple, and he said it was just because he put so much love into the making.

At last Amati died and his pupil took his place as the master violin-maker of Italy. Salvator and Gulio's voices had become squeaky, and people no longer cared to hear them, but still Antonio kept steadily on at his much-loved work, trying to make each violin better and more beautiful than the one before it.

That was over two hundred years ago, and now, at the mention of Cremona, men think not of the fair city beside the Po, whose stately Duomo still looks out over the fertile plains of Lombardy, but of the world's greatest violin-maker, Antonio Strad-ivarius. There is no civilized land into which his instruments have not been taken, for musicians prize them more highly than any others, and refuse for them sums greater than any of which the boy Antonio had ever heard. To own a "Strad" is to be rich indeed, and one of the things of which Italy is proudest is that it was the land of Antonio Strad-ivarius. All of which goes to show that although one can do nothing but whittle, he may help to make music for the world if there is a song in the heart, and a noble purpose and patience and persistence keep the hands at work.

From *Boyhood Stories of Famous Men*, by KATHERINE DUNLAP CATHER. Copyright, 1916. Used by permission of the publishers, The Century Company, New York.

XI

THE CHILDREN'S CRUSADE

THE air was drowsy with the perfume of the late spring flowers and with the hum of insects. Now and then the sound of a bell, tinkling softly, came from over the brow of the low hill, where sheep were grazing in the pastures. A shepherd lad, his head pillowed on the shaggy side of his dog, stirred restlessly, and then suddenly sprang to his feet. With a word to his dog, and a quick command to his sheep he started on his way toward the village.

The animals did not like being driven away from the sweet new grass, for the sun was still high in the sky. But the boy was firm, and soon the little flock, guarded by the well-trained dog, was being herded along the road well on the way to the village. The sight of the shepherd lad returning from the pastures so early in the day sent many people hurrying out to ask the reason.

"O Stephen," called a boy who came running out of a house, "why art thou back so early? Canst thou come with me down to the stream?"

Then for the first time Stephen, the shepherd lad, spoke, and in a soft voice answered his friend's question:

"Jacques, I have news for thee. This day I have had a dream that told me I could be the leader of a great Crusade to Jerusalem, the Holy City, to the land where lived Jesus Christ, our Lord. Thou knowest, Jacques, how many years ago the Holy

City fell into the hands of the Turks, and how our fathers have gone on long journeys to Palestine that they might win back the place where our Lord lived. Even now Pope Innocent is trying to gather an army to march against Jerusalem. It is for us, the children of France, to go forth and serve our Lord."

As he spoke his voice soared higher and higher with feeling. The curious men who were standing by either laughed at the boy or grew angry. "What foolishness!" they exclaimed. "Can a mere boy lead a crusade against the Turks, when strong men have failed?"

In answer Jacques stepped quickly to the side of Stephen. "Wilt thou take me, Stephen?" he said. "I am ready."

"For God and for our Lord," cried the lads. "To the Holy Land! To the Holy Land!" And soon the cry was taken up by all the children standing near.

Days of toil passed quickly, and as Stephen and his followers traveled from village to village, more children were added to their number. Sometimes, when Stephen had been in a city for only a few hours, all the children would leave their homes to join the Crusade.

"Shall we allow the Turks to rule over our Holy City? Shame on us, if we do!" And like steel particles to a magnet, children flocked to the challenge. Southward they took their course, to the old French city of Marseilles. As they went, Stephen told them stories of the Saviour in whose service they had enlisted—stories of how Jesus had blessed the children, of how he had gone about helping people and doing deeds of kindness. Always Stephen would finish his story with, "Can we fail Him now? No, we must serve Him with our best!" Always came back the answer, "For Jesus our Lord! On to Palestine."

As the children's band marched through the fields and villages of France, the sun glistened on the slender blood-red crosses which they always wore on their breasts. Sometimes a child too weak for the long march dropped silently from the ranks. But over hill and through valley tramped the throng, and over all rang out the Crusaders' Hymn:

"Fairest Lord Jesus! Ruler of all nature!
    O thou of God and man the Son!
Thee will I cherish, Thee will I honor,
    Thee, my soul's glory, joy, and crown.

"Fair are the meadows, fairer still the woodlands,
    Robed in the blooming garb of spring;
Jesus is fairer, Jesus is purer,
    Who makes the woeful heart to sing.

"Fair is the sunshine, fairer still the moonlight,
    And all the twinkling starry host;
Jesus shines brighter, Jesus shines purer
    Than all the angels heaven can boast."

At last they reached the shores of the blue Mediterranean Sea, but they had not been there long before a fearful storm arose. The thunder rolled and the lightning flashed. A fleet of ships came swiftly toward the land, but only a few of them could ride safe at anchor. The others were dashed against the rocks.

Still the cry, "On to Jerusalem! For Jesus our Lord!" sounded over the waves, but the children's band never reached the Holy City. They were taken to Egypt by a band of traders, but when word came back to Pope Innocent that the children had landed safely in Egypt, he was able to rally a great army of men for the Fifth Crusade. "The very children," he cried in scorn, "have gladly fought to conquer the Holy Land."

So it was that seven hundred years ago the children of France bravely gave their lives to win back Jerusalem from the Turks. And now children all over this great world are following and serving the Christ. Their cry is still, "For God and for our Lord!" and with their whole hearts and by their service they are showing their love for him.

XII

WHERE LOVE IS, THERE GOD IS

In the city lived Martin, a shoemaker. He lived in a basement, in a little room with one window. The window looked out on the street. Through the window he used to watch the people passing by. Although only the feet could be seen, yet by the boots Martin knew their owners. He had lived long in one place, and few pairs of boots in his district had not been in his hands at some time or other. He was never out of work because all knew that he did his work well and kept his promises.

He lived all alone in his basement. His wife had died and also his children, so he was glad to watch the people passing on the street, just for company. At night, when his work was done, he would take a New Testament in large print from a high shelf and read until all the kerosene in his lamp had burned out.

Once it happened that Martin read until late into the night. He was reading the Gospel of Luke; and he came to the verses:

"And unto him that smiteth thee on the one cheek offer also the other; and him that taketh away thy cloak forbid not to take thy coat also.

"Give to every man that asketh of thee; and of him that taketh away thy goods ask them not again.

"And as ye would that men should do to you, do ye also to them likewise."

And then he read about the Pharisee who asked
Jesus to supper and then was not kind to him.

Martin took off his spectacles, put them down
upon the book, and thought to himself:

"That Pharisee must have been such a man as
I am. I, too, have thought only of myself, how I
might have my tea, be warm and comfortable, but
never to think about my guest. He thought about
himself, but there was not the least care taken of
the guest. And who was his guest? The Lord himself. If he had come to me, should I have done the
same way?"

Martin rested his head upon both his arms, and
did not notice how he fell fast asleep.

"Martin!" suddenly seemed to sound in his
ears.

Martin started in his sleep: "Who is here?"

Again he fell into a doze. Suddenly he plainly
heard:

"Martin! Ah, Martin! look to-morrow on the
street. I am coming."

Martin awoke, rose from the chair, began to rub
his eyes. He did not know whether he had heard
the words in a dream or in reality. He turned down
the light and went to bed.

At daybreak next morning, Martin rose, said his
prayer to God, lighted the stove, put on the soup
to cook and water to heat, tied on his shoemaker's
apron, and sat down by the window to work.

As he worked, he thought about his dream of the
night before; and now, when any one passed, he
bent down so that he could see not only the feet
but also the face. Presently there came alongside
of the window an old street-cleaner with a shovel

in his hands. Martin knew him by his felt boots.
The old man's name was Stephen; and a neighbor-
ing merchant, out of charity, gave him a home with
him. Stephen began to shovel away the snow from
in front of Martin's window. Then he stopped
and leaned his shovel against the wall. He was an
old, broken-down man; evidently he had not
strength enough even to shovel snow. Martin said
to himself: "I will give him some tea. The water
must be boiling by this time." He laid down his
awl, put the hot water on the table, made the tea,
and tapped with his finger on the glass. Stephen
turned around and came to the window. Martin
beckoned to him, and went to open the door.

"Come in, warm yourself a little," he said. "You
must be cold."

"May Christ reward you for this! My bones
ache," said Stephen. He came in, shook off the
snow, tried to wipe his feet so as not to soil the
floor, but staggered.

"Don't trouble to wipe your feet. I will clean
up the snow myself; we are used to such things.
Come in and sit down," said Martin. "Drink a
cup of tea."

The two men had their tea together, but Stephen
noticed that Martin kept looking out on the street.

"Are you expecting anyone?" he asked.

Then Martin told him how he had been reading
about the Pharisee who did not receive Christ with
honor, and how he had had a dream in which he
had heard Christ say that he was coming to see
him that day, and how it had got into his head
so that he could not think of anything else. Then
he saw that Stephen's cup was empty and asked him

to have some more tea. But Stephen rose and shook his head.

"Thank you, Martin," he said, "for treating me so kindly."

"You are welcome; come in again; always glad to see a friend," said Martin.

A little later, Martin saw a woman pass his window with a child in her arms. She stopped and stood by the wall with her back to the wind, and he saw that she was dressed in shabby summer clothes and had nothing to wrap the child in. From behind the glass he could hear the child crying. He hurried to the door and cried, "Here, my good woman!" The woman heard him and turned around.

"Why are you standing in the cold with the child? Come into my room where it is warm: you can manage it better. Right in this way!"

The woman was astonished, but she followed Martin, who let her into the room and to a chair.

"There," he said, "sit down, my good woman, nearer to the stove where you can get warm."

Then he went to the stove, poured some hot soup into a dish and put it on the table.

"Sit down and eat," he said to the woman, "and I will mind the little one. You see, I once had children of my own; I know how to handle them."

The woman sat down at the table and ate the soup while Martin minded the baby. In the meantime she told him her story. Her husband had gone to hunt work and she had not heard from him for seven months. She had been a cook, but was now three months without a place. Now she had nothing to eat and had pawned her last shawl so that she had no warm clothes.

Martin went to the wall where his own clothes hung and succeeded in finding an old coat. He gave it to the woman.

"It is a poor thing," he said, "yet you may put it to some use."

The woman burst into tears as she took the coat.

"May God bless you!" she cried. "He must have sent me himself to your window. My little child would have frozen to death."

Martin smiled. "Indeed he must have sent you," he said; and then he remembered his dream of the night before—he had forgotten it in his care for the woman. He told her of it—how he had heard the voice, how Christ had promised to come to see him that day.

"All things are possible," said the woman. She rose, put on the coat, wrapped up her little child in it; and as she started to go, she thanked Martin again.

"Take this, for Christ's sake," said Martin, giving her a piece of money. "Get back your shawl." Then he went with her to the door.

The window grew darker, but Martin still watched as he worked. For some time there was nothing out of the ordinary. Then an old apple woman stopped right in front of his window. Only a few apples were left in her basket, and over her shoulder she carried a bag full of chips. She must have gathered them up in some new building and was on her way home. The bag was so heavy that she wanted to shift it to the other shoulder. So she lowered the bag upon the sidewalk, stood the basket with the apples on a little post, and began to shake down the splinters in the bag. And while she was shaking her bag, a little boy with a torn cap came along, picked up an apple from the basket, and was about to run away; but the old woman noticed it and caught him by the sleeve. The boy began to struggle, but the old woman grasped him with both hands, knocked off his cap, and caught him by the hair.

Martin rushed out to the street. "I did not take it!" he heard the boy say. "Let me go!"

"Let him go," said Martin, taking the boy by the arm. "Forgive him for Christ's sake."

The old woman let him loose. The boy tried to run, but Martin held him back.

"Ask the little grandmother's forgiveness," he said, "and don't you ever do it again. I saw you take the apple."

With tears in his eyes the boy began to ask forgiveness.

"That's right; and now, here's an apple for you." Martin got an apple from the basket, and gave it to the boy. "I will pay you for both, little grandmother," he said to the woman.

The old woman could not understand at first. She thought the boy ought to be punished so that he would remember it for a whole week. But Martin told her that he ought to be forgiven, as he had only been thoughtless and was sorry.

"Of course, it is a childish trick. God be with him," said she, pointing to the boy.

She was just about to lift the bag to her shoulder when the boy ran up and said, "Let me carry it, little grandmother; it is on my way."

The old woman nodded her head and put the bag on the boy's back.

Side by side they both passed along the street.

And the old woman had not even allowed Martin to pay for the apples.

Martin stood gazing after them until they disappeared. Then he returned to his room, and as it was dark, he put away his work, lighted the lamp, and took the Gospesl down from the shelf. He intended to open the book at the very place where he had yesterday put a piece of leather as a mark, but it happened to open at another place; and the moment he opened the Testament, he remembered last night's dream. And as soon as he remembered it, it seemed as though he heard some one stepping about behind him. He looked around and there, in the dark corner, it seemed as though people were standing: he was at a loss to know who they were. And a voice whispered in his ear:

"Martin, ah, Martin! did you not recognize me?"

"Who?" uttered Martin.

Then he seemed to see Stephen, and the women and the child, and the old apple woman with the boy. One by one, they stepped out of the dark corner, smiled at him, and vanished.

Martin was glad as he thought of them. He put on his spectacles, and began to read the Bible where it had happened to open. On the upper part of the page he read:

"For I was an hungered, and ye gave me meat: I was thirsty, and ye gave me drink: I was a stranger, and ye took me in. . . ."

And on the lower part of the page he read this:

"Inasmuch as ye have done it unto one of the least of these my brethren, ye have done it unto me."

And Martin understood that his dream did not deceive him; that Christ had really visited him that day, and that he really received him.

Adapted from Count Tolstoy, from the translation by Nathan Haskell Dole. From *Living Together*, by FRANCES M. DADMUN. Used by permission of the publishers, The Beacon Press.

XIII

RAGGEDY ANDREW

It all happened far across the sea in that distant country called India. The rainy season had come, and sometimes it seemed as though the very sea itself were being turned upside down over the land. Out of doors the drenching rain made life uncomfortable, but inside a small house that stood in the center of a clearing in the jungle, there was the suffering and agony that comes with dangerous sickness.

The woman who lay, almost unconscious from pain, upon the low bed, made in the Indian fashion only a few inches from the floor, was a doctor who had come across thousands of miles to serve the Hindu women. And due to overwork and poor living conditions, she had become very sick. There she lay, alone, her life almost gone, twenty miles from any other people. Hours before, her only servant had left on the long and dangerous journey to the nearest doctor, bearing a scrawled note, "Operation necessary—come at once."

Near the bed, a tiny white dog sat on guard. He was one of those long-haired little fellows, a kind of poodle, sometimes spoken of jokingly as a "dish-mop." But a very intelligent dish-mop he was. Occasionally he left his post to move nearer his mistress and lick her hand, and always a quiver of relief passed over her suffering-worn face at his touch.

For three years now Raggedy Andrew, called "Raggs" for short, had been the doctor's companion. She had found him on one of her trips to a large Indian city, and a sorry little creature he had been! But good care and tenderness had transformed the little beast into a living bundle of life and affection for his mistress.

An hour had passed with no movement from the unconscious form on the bed. "Raggs" had not once given up his post beside his mistress. Suddenly, his floppy ears gave a quick, jerky movement, his black eyes seemed turned to staring black beads. He gave an agonized bark, and then another—short and frenzied. There, on the floor, not seven feet away, glistened the coils and the large flat head of a cobra! Slowly, but surely, it was moving forward, nearer the woman lying on the bed, its eyes fixed upon the beady eyes of "Raggs."

The frightened yelping of the dog shocked the woman to consciousness. Weakly she moved her head, until she could see the poodle, making quick leaps forward, each jump accompanied by a short, fierce bark. Too weak to lift her head, she could only lie there, wondering, and noticing that with each leap "Raggs" was being forced to retreat, nearer to her bed.

At last, he was but about two feet from her face, and then she saw the sinister flat head of the cobra!

For hours, the doctor lay unconscious, but at last she opened her eyes. There, sitting very near her, was the familiar form of "Raggs," tense watchfulness in every part of his body. Weakly the woman moved her head, and the motion brought her servant to her side.

"Oh, Miss Sahib," he said, "you are better?" He forced a bit of liquid within her lips, and watched with joy as a flush of color came over his mistress' cheeks. Weakly she tried to speak, and as he bent nearer, he caught the words, "Raggs—cobra."

"Oh, Miss Sahib," the servant said, "the man doctor and I got here just in time. He shot the snake just as it was ready to strike 'Raggs,' who was standing only six inches from your shoulder!"

And the little "dish-mop," hearing his name, moved quickly to his mistress and licked her hand as she weakly tried to pat his head.

XIV

THE MERCHANTS AND THE GOLDEN BOWL

Two merchants were crossing a river. On the opposite bank lay the city where they were going to sell their wares. They were not partners, but they agreed to divide the streets of the city between them. They also agreed that when one of them had gone through all the streets of his division, the other might follow and sell what he could, since the things they had to sell were not alike.

One of the merchants could hardly wait for the boat to land. He was the first to leap on shore, and he plunged at once into the nearest street of his division, where he began crying: "Waterpots to sell. Waterpots to sell."

Presently he came to a house which looked promising. It was large and well built, and it seemed to him that a family who could afford to live in such a house ought to buy a good deal. But it happened that the people in this house were poor. They had been rich once, to be sure, but now their money was gone, and the strong men who had earned it were dead. There were left only an old woman and her granddaughter, who got their living by working out.

When the little girl heard the merchant's voice in the street she said,

"O Grandmother, I do wish I could have something—a ring, perhaps, which ought not to cost very much."

"We have no money, dear, for anything," said the grandmother, "and what could we give in exchange for it?"

"Here's an old bowl," said the girl; "it's of no use to us. Let us change that for it."

The bowl did look very old and useless. It was crusted over with dirt which had been hardened in the fire and would not wash off. It was so black that neither the grandmother nor the little girl knew that the bowl had been bought when the family was rich, and that it was really made of gold.

The merchant was invited in and given a seat. Then the grandmother showed him the bowl and asked if he would exchange it for a ring or some other little trinket for the child.

Now the merchant had handled many bowls, and he knew as soon as he lifted it that it was better than it looked. To make sure, he turned it over, and scratching it on the bottom with a needle, saw that it was gold. But he was a mean man, and had no intention of paying the grandmother what it was worth. Instead, he hoped to get it for nothing.

"What is the value of this!" he exclaimed. "It isn't worth a cent!"

He threw it on the floor and left the house, expecting to be called back; but the grandmother took him at his word.

"It is just what I thought, dear," she said; "it is good for nothing. I am sorry about the ring."

Later in the day, the second merchant came through that street.

"O Grandmother!" said the girl, "this man looks kinder than the other. Let us ask him about the bowl."

The merchant was invited in, and examined the bowl as the first had done.

"Why!" he said at once. "This bowl is pure gold. It is worth one hundred thousand pieces of money. All the money and goods I have with me would not pay for it."

The astonished grandmother did not know what to say at first. Then she told him of the other merchant who had said the bowl was worth nothing.

"It must be your goodness that has turned the bowl to gold," she said. "Do take it and give us something or other. We shall be satisfied."

At last she persuaded the honest merchant to take the bowl, but he insisted upon leaving with them everything he had in his bag, keeping only the bag itself, his scales, and enough money to pay the ferryman.

After he had gone, the first merchant returned. He said that he had changed his mind about the bowl and was willing to give them a little for it—a ring, perhaps, for the child, if it were not too expensive.

"You dishonest man!" cried the grandmother. "That was a golden bowl and you knew it, although I did not. But now you are too late. Another merchant, more honest than you are, has given all he had for it."

The dishonest merchant did not stop to ask questions. He ran as fast as he could go to the river.

"It should have been my bowl," he muttered as he ran. "I saw it first. I will take it from him if I catch him."

When he reached the bank, the ferryman and the other merchant were already half-way across.

"Come back! Come back!" called the angry man on shore.

But the ferryman did not turn; he kept straight on.

The dishonest merchant saw his former companion land on the opposite shore and disappear down the road. Through his meanness in telling a lie to a poor old woman and a little girl, he had lost the golden bowl forever.

(Adapted from the Jataka.)   From *Living Together*, by FRANCES M. DADMUN.   Used by permission of the publishers, The Beacon Press.

XV

THE MIRACULOUS PITCHER

ONE evening long ago, old Philemon and his old wife Baucis sat at their cottage door enjoying the sunset. They had already eaten their simple supper, and intended now to spend a quiet hour or two before bedtime. But the rude shouts of children and the fierce barking of dogs in the village near by grew louder and louder, until at last it was hardly possible for Baucis and Philemon to hear each other speak.

"I never heard the dogs so loud," said the good old man.

"Nor the children so rude," answered his good old wife.

The noise came nearer and nearer until, at the foot of the little hill on which their cottage stood, they saw two travelers approaching on foot. Close behind them came the fierce dogs, snarling at their very heels. A little farther off ran a crowd of children, who sent up shrill cries and flung stones at the two strangers with all their might.

Both of the travelers were poorly dressed, and looked as if they might not have enough money in their pockets to pay for a night's lodging. And this, I am afraid, was the reason why the village people had allowed their children and dogs to treat them so rudely.

"Come, wife," said Philemon to Baucis, "let us go

and meet these poor people. They must feel almost too discouraged to climb the hill."

"Do you go and meet them," answered Baucis, "while I hurry indoors and see if we can get them anything for supper. A comfortable bowl of bread and milk would do wonders toward raising their spirits."

So Baucis hastened into the cottage, and Philemon, holding out his hand to the travelers, said in the heartiest tone you can imagine,

"Welcome, strangers! welcome!"

"Thank you!" replied the younger. "This is quite another greeting than we have met with in the village. Why do you live in such a bad neighborhood?"

"I suppose," said old Philemon, smiling, "that I was put here to make up for the impoliteness of my neighbors."

"Truly, we need it," said the traveler, laughing. "Those children, little rascals, have spattered us finely with their mud balls, and one of the curs has torn my coat, which was ragged enough already. But I hit him over the muzzle with my staff, and you must have heard him yelp even as far off as this."

By this time Philemon and his two guests had reached the cottage door.

"Friends," said the old man, "sit down and rest yourselves here on this bench. My good wife Baucis has gone to see what you can have for supper. We are poor folks, but you are welcome to whatever we have in the cupboard."

While Baucis was getting supper, the travelers talked with Philemon. The younger, who said his name was Quicksilver, was very amusing and kept

Philemon laughing. The older was so kind that Philemon wanted to tell him about everything he cared for most.

Baucis had now got supper ready, and coming to the door, began to make apologies because there was so little.

"If we had known you were coming," said she, "my good man and myself would have gone without a morsel. But I took most of to-day's milk to make cheese, and our last loaf is half eaten."

"Do not trouble yourself," said the older stranger, kindly. "An honest, hearty welcome is better than the finest food."

"A welcome you shall have," cried Baucis, "as well as a little honey that we happen to have left, and a bunch of purple grapes besides."

"Why, Mother Baucis, it is a feast!" exclaimed Quicksilver, laughing, "an absolute feast! and you shall see how bravely I will play my part at it. I think I never felt hungrier in my life."

"Mercy on us!" whispered Baucis to her husband. "If the young man has such a terrible appetite, I am afraid there will not be half enough for supper."

They all went into the cottage.

As Baucis had said, there was not much for two hungry travelers. In the middle of the table was part of a brown loaf, with a piece of cheese on one side of it and a dish of honeycomb on the other. There was a pretty good bunch of grapes for each of the guests. An earthen pitcher nearly full of milk stood at a corner of the table, and when Baucis had filled two bowls and set them before the strangers, only a little milk remained in the bottom of the pitcher.

Poor Baucis kept wishing she might starve for a week if only there might be more for her guests; but since the supper was so very small, she could not help wishing that their appetites were not quite so large. They drank all the milk in their bowls at once, and then Quicksilver asked for more.

"Now, my dear people," answered Baucis, "I am so sorry and ashamed! But the truth is, there is hardly a drop more milk in the pitcher. O, husband! husband! why didn't we go without supper?"

"Why, it is not so bad as that," cried Quicksilver; "there is certainly more milk in the pitcher."

And taking the pitcher by the handle, he filled both their bowls. Baucis could hardly believe her eyes.

"What excellent milk!" said Quicksilver, emptying his bowl a second time. "Excuse me, my kind hostess, but I must really ask you for a little more."

Now Baucis knew that the pitcher was empty this time, for she had seen Quicksilver turn it upside down, but in order to let him see it, she took up the pitcher and pretended to pour milk into his bowl. How surprised she was when the milk came out so fast that it not only filled the bowl, but was spilled on the table!

"And now a slice of your brown loaf, Mother Baucis," said Quicksilver, "and a little of that honey."

Baucis cut him a slice, and although the loaf had been dry and crusty when she and her husband had eaten it, it was now as light and moist as if a few hours out of the oven. She could not but think that there was something unusual in what had been going on. So, after helping her guests to bread and honey, and laying a bunch of grapes by each of their plates, she sat down by Philemon and told him in a whisper what she had seen.

Now Philemon thought Baucis had been mistaken, especially about the pitcher; so when Quicksilver asked for yet another bowl of milk, Philemon jumped up and took the pitcher himself. He peeped in and saw for a certainty that there was not a single drop of milk in it. Then, all at once, a little, white fountain gushed up from the bottom of the pitcher and filled it to the brim with foaming milk. It was lucky that Philemon, in his surprise, did not drop the miraculous pitcher from his hand.

"Who are ye, wonder-working strangers?" cried he, even more bewildered than his wife had been.

"Your guests, my good Philemon, and your friends," replied the elder traveler; "give me also a bowl of the milk; and may your pitcher never be empty for kind Baucis and yourself, any more than for the needy traveler."

Nor was it. The guests went away the next morning, leaving Philemon and Baucis, but the pitcher was never empty when it was desirable to have it full. Whenever an honest, good-humored, and generous guest drank from it, he found it the sweetest fluid he had ever tasted, but if a cross and disagreeable man happened to sip, he was pretty certain to make a wry face and call it a pitcher of sour milk. As for Philemon and Baucis, it was a joy to them to have such a pitcher, since now they could be hospitable to their heart's content, and no poor traveler need ever go from their door thirsty.

Adapted from Nathaniel Hawthorne. From *Living Together*, by FRANCES M. DADMUN. Used by permission of the publishers, The Beacon Press.

XVI

THEY WHO FIND AMERICA

AWAY, away through the night flew a little cloud, its filmy streamers floating out behind. It flew over the tops of the trees and over the rivers and meadows, until at last below it there was nothing but tall buildings. It brushed against great shadowy office buildings, then flew on, waving to the sparkling lights that winked and twinkled so roguishly on broad, lighted streets. It passed over a great section of buildings that looked like square boxes with rows and rows of lighted shelves, each shelf divided into pigeon-holes. In the shelves lived the people of the city, all tucked away at night, each in the little section he called his own home.

Then the cloud flew where the apartments grew smaller and darker, and the smaller they grew the more people crowded into the corners, and these "shelves" were called the tenements of the great city. Here the little cloud settled down on a narrow iron stairway, a fire escape, at the top floor of one of these tenements. A tiny window gave a peep into a small room where a light burned dimly. There were dozens of aprons, a whole heap of blue ones cluttered in a disconsolate heap on the floor. Piled high on a table were apron strings, and nearby sat a little girl sewing as fast as her fingers could fly. She was fastening the strings on to the aprons. Beside her sat a little Italian woman sewing also.

Neither had spoken for ever and ever so long. At last the mother laid down her work with a sigh and looked at the little figure bent over the apron strings. "Little Liza, how long and fast you have sewed! You must be very tired." It was hours that they had sat there working.

The mother rose wearily and went to cover more closely two children who lay feet to feet on a low couch. It was cold in the dimly lighted room. All day there had been no coal to put in the little stove.

"I wonder where it is," she sighed as she resumed her seat, her voice full of weariness.

"What, Mother?" Liza stopped, too, and stretched her stiff little hands.

"I have thought often that it is lost," confessed the dark little woman. "Surely this is not the America we heard of before we came here. It is not the land which they told us in Italy, but a country of strange, hard ways. There are none who try to understand when one asks the way. They brush one and go on. They are all hurrying. Even the food is not good. I was never troubled over my babies in Italy. They grew rosy and fat eating what we all ate. But now—poor little Nickie is so thin he is like to blow away. Yes, it is a country with strange, hard ways," she repeated sadly.

"Mother, I wonder if it is we who are lost and not America. I think the America we heard of is here somewhere—only we have not found it. At the Friendly House, you know—"

She was interrupted by the entrance of Tito. He flung his cap on the table where Liza rescued it quickly from being entirely lost in the pile of apron strings. There was not a spot in the room that was not piled high with something—it was such a very small room for six people to live in!

"Well, Tito, where is your father? He never comes home any more," wailed the mother.

"I guess he is afraid to come, for he has no money to bring home for you and the children. They have no more money to give out at the meetings as they did at first. He does not even go to them because he cannot understand."

"Where is he, then? But why do I ask? I know what he is doing. He is with that crowd of men who get drink secretly. But what is it that makes you seem glad?" she added impatiently. "I know you have had nothing to eat, though that you try to keep from us. My poor Tito," she moaned, softening, "you were ever a brave lad. What gives you courage in this strange land?"

"I cannot describe it, Mother, but at the meetings of the men I feel that I am not alone in this big country. I feel that there are men and boys who mean to stand by each other. They will some day make things better in the dusty shop, and we will have more food and coal in our homes. We may even find somewhere something beautiful. I cannot tell how I feel it, but as I listen and every night come to know more of what the strange tongues say, I know I was right in coming out of the shop."

"Then the men did not gather around you and tell you to come out as they did your father?"

"No, I was young and in another room of the work. The boss man of my room comes to me and offers me more money in the envelope if I do not go. I go out from the factory thinking hard, and I meet the men so eager, so full of joy that everything is settled and they are going to have something to do. I ask all about it and I have many answers. Some say there will be no more dust from the stone we cut to choke the throat, others think it will mean more milk for *bambinos*, others know it will mean we can buy shoes and clothes. One man who speaks Italian asked me about our family and how long we are from the home country. Then I think that this must be the America that we heard of where people work together."

"Oh, we all believed much when we came," said the mother bitterly, "but see how we live!"

"I know, Mother, but such is the way they all talk at the meeting. They asked to-night if there were any in great need. I didn't understand until the man next to me explained later, and then they had taken all the names. They want to help. I should have stayed until the meeting was over, for some seem to think more good news will come before many hours, but I was so tired."

"Ah, my poor little boy," sighed his mother. Tito was tall and large for his age, so the factory had taken him even though he was a year under the youngest working age.

The baby coughed and cried. The mother hurriedly dipped the corner of her handkerchief in some sweetened water and ran to put it in the child's mouth.

"We must get something. There's nothing left to eat and no coal for two days," whispered Liza to her brother. "I have thought of going to the Friendly House."

"The Friendly House!" exclaimed the mother, rejoining them. "It is always the Friendly House. She comes back and says we must put shining oily cloth on the table and eat there, washing it off each day, nay, after every meal. Have they nothing better to do?"

"You know I have told you many things. It was the music on that Sunday that carried me up the stairs, though I was so scared I hardly knew what I was doing. You know yourself how much better I speak the English since I have learned of them. They too speak of things as Tito does. I think they are wanting good for everybody," finished the little girl rallying to the defense of the Church House. Again the baby cried. The boy, who had flung himself on the one bed in the room, pulled himself up with a jerk.

"Come, we must do something. I think I can find the way to go to father if Liza will come with me. He is always gentle with her."

"Go out alone at night with only your young brother?" exclaimed the mother, turning to Liza.

"All the girls do that here, mother. I will be back very soon." Liza smoothed the hair from the worn forehead and pressed her young red lips on the rough skin, as her mother threw her shawl around the child.

"A strange country indeed!" The tired little mother summed up all the puzzled perplexity and pain of her mind in the short phrase that she repeated dully. "A strange country indeed!"

"We will yet find America," called Liza from the landing.

The two children slipped down the five flights of dark stairs—the glimmer of their mother's light, held high for them, grew fainter, then darkness swallowed it up completely and they stumbled out from the last flight into the street.

Neither spoke, for each was struggling to be brave. The less said, the better, they thought.

Tito led the way through back alleys and narrow streets. High heaps of snow here and there had gathered to themselves by a sort of mutual attraction tin cans, fruit peelings, odds and ends of food and belongings that always collect in such places.

They hurried along, Tito knocking his chapped hands together to keep warm. At the corner they turned upon a better-lighted street. A lady crossed from the opposite side and walked just ahead of them. Suddenly she turned, as if she had dropped something. The children came to a standstill beside her, and Tito stopped quickly, running his hand over the ground to pick up anything which might have fallen.

Then everything happened in a flash. She said something in a harsh, quick voice, and Tito darted away. What she said, Liza could not understand, probably Tito did not, but she raised her voice and shouted. Two policemen came running around the corner.

What the trouble was, Liza did not know, but she ran, her brother ran, the policemen ran shouting English that would have challenged anyone to understand. As they rounded a dark corner, Liza stepped back into a doorway, breathless and panting. Around the next corner went the others, but Tito's quick feet outdid them and he gained his own street with no one in sight. He bounded up the stairs, without turning to see the big policeman's figure as it dashed into view at that moment.

Only a few seconds passed between the boy's swift entrance to his home and the heavy thud of the police as they bustled into the wretched tenement and bolted the door behind them. The little mother wept hysterically as these representatives of the law took possession of her home. The children awoke to add their bit to the noise and confusion. Tito stood sullen, trying to make out what the men were saying. "No! No!" he put in dramatically in lulls between their heated words. When they had finished searching the room, even the previous lack of order was as nothing to the chaos they had created.

Tito, they took away with them and left the frightened woman wringing her hands and wailing as only Italian women can. Neighbors peered in, but withdrew—the police had been there.

"Tito, Tito," moaned the mother, "where have they taken him? And my little Liza, too, is lost!" She beat her breast.

From where Liza crouched, she could see the woman still looking on the ground. Presently she went on a few steps and then stopped to talk to another policeman who had come upon the scene. A few minutes later around the corner appeared the two policemen and Tito with them. They were talking loudly and unintelligibly to the boy as they passed. Then there was silence again in the little alley and only the chance passer-by crossed the corner where the sad mix-up had occurred.

The truth of what had happened dawned slowly on Liza. The lady had dropped something, had thought Tito and she had taken it, and now they must be taking her brother to jail. What would happen to him? Her mind was filled with frightened images of Tito behind the bars in some dark dungeon. The numb coldness that gripped her made it hard to think or act. She must do something. Perhaps what the lady lost was still there. Oh, if she could find it and save Tito!

She ran to the spot and knelt on the cold, ice-crusted pavement, feeling over the surface with her little bare fingers. Nothing there! A dozen people had passed since the occurrence. What hope was there! But she bent over the edge of the curb, running her fingers through a crack that ran between the pavement and the frozen pile of snow shoveled into the street. A jagged point—a piece of ice—no, it was too hard for that. It moved, yes, she had it now out on her hand. Not a piece of ice at all, but a lovely thing that shone and sparkled as it hung from a tiny chain.

A heavy hand came down on the child's shoulder, so hard that Liza almost dropped the precious thing she had just found.

"What, still here?" said a man's voice. "And you were the one that had it all along! He gave it to you, eh, and ran?"

The girl looked at him with her great dark eyes full of bewilderment. She could not understand all he said, but she understood the accusing tone and shook her head. "No, no, I find. Tito where?" she questioned.

"You'll find out fast enough, just this way please." The man meant to be kindly, but he spoke in the loud voice that people use in speaking to foreigners. They try to gain understanding by dint of noise.

Liza went with him willingly enough, for it meant going to Tito.

It was not until the next morning, however, that they met in the children's court. Things looked dark for the two, even when Liza was produced.

In broken words, using all her newly gained English, Liza tried to explain. She was puzzled indeed. Bravely she had left her hiding place to hunt the piece of evidence that would free Tito. Now things seemed worse than ever. She had done no good. She was on the verge of tears. Would no one understand, no one believe her? Mother was right, it was a strange, hard country. With the thought of the little mother waiting so scared at home, Liza gulped and the last word ended with a sob. She put her hands over her flaming face.

She did not see the quiet-looking woman who had walked up the aisle and stood waiting to speak a word. The judge turned to her as he often had turned before with a sigh of relief.

"I know this little girl. She comes to our church classes. I think she is telling the truth, trying to tell it. Let me ask her to tell me the story in her own language."

With the first words of that quiet, kindly voice that she had heard before, Liza looked up. She would have run to the woman, had she not been so frightened. Under the persuasive questioning of one who seemed to understand, Liza told the whole mixed-up story.

When translated to the judge, it seemed sensible enough. And then, too, these children did not look like thieves. Their faces were bright and honest, though sadly pinched now with cold, hunger, and fear.

"Will you be responsible for them?" the judge asked the lady.

"Yes, gladly," she replied.

They left the court, one on either side of their new friend, and it seemed to Tito and Liza as if they were walking in a dream.

"You have not been to us for many days, Liza. What has been the matter?"

"I sew—working home," explained Liza. "Men no job." The strike again, thought the worker. The little girl's cheeks seemed thinner than usual. How many had suffered these cold winter days!

Just then a man passed the three. He was walking with a buoyant step, his head held high. He noticed Tito and stopped to say: "Heard the news? It has just come—this morning. It is all fixed up. Not all we ask for, but pretty good, and every man back at his job to-morrow."

Vaguely Tito and Liza took in more from his actions than from his words.

"I go to tell the men so we will all be in our places to-morrow." He threw up his cap for joy as he went on. Tito threw up his cap, too, with a quick burst of Italian feeling.

As they walked toward the tenement in which they lived, the lady talked with them in their own tongue, and discovered their needs. She saw to it that they carried home with them milk for the baby and a loaf of bread for themselves.

The icy hand of the little girl, laid on her warm one as they climbed the dark flight of stairs, made her ask, "Have you no coat, Liza, that you are so cold?"

"No," answered Liza simply. How good the lady was to care!

"When you come around to the house to-day I must see if there is a coat and some mittens for you that other American children have passed on, as one does in a big family to the younger ones who are growing up."

"American children?" murmured Liza wonderingly. "They bring things there?"

"Yes, indeed. Tito must come, too," went on the lady. "Bring him, Liza, to the Friendly House."

"I have wanted him to come," said Liza, "for he can sing, and he could be with the boys who lead the songs."

"There are many things he could do with other boys who are all learning to be real Americans."

"What is this place?" asked Tito abruptly.

With a wisdom she did not herself realize, the lady answered slowly in almost the boy's own words. "It is a spot where people work together for each other. People who know English and people who don't, come there. Boys and girls who have much in books and clothes and toys share them with those who have little. They do not want anyone in America to need things or anyone to stand alone. And your mother, there are many mothers who come there, too, with their babies, and—"

"Oh, mother!" they had reached the top floor of the tenement by this time. Liza stumbled in without explanation or introduction of the visitor. "The Friendly House is for you, too, and for Tito. I, also, thought America was lost last night, but this friend has come who will show us the way. Now we can all find America together!"

From "Stay-at-Home Journeys," by AGNES WILSON OSBORNE. Used by permission of the publishers, Council of Women for Home Missions and Missionary Education Movement of the United States and Canada.

XVII

FRIDAY'S FOOTPRINTS

THEY were astonishingly big footprints! And our little Miss Robinson Crusoe didn't like the looks of them one bit. For it was rather dreadful discovering footprints all by yourself off in the jungle forest, when you hadn't started out to play Babe-in-the-Woods, but had somehow gotten lost on the aimless little trails that all looked exactly alike.

She gulped hard and decided that whatever came she must not cry, but she couldn't deny that the footprints got to looking bigger and bigger the farther she followed them. This was what came of disobeying mother, and being perfectly sure you knew the trail home when you didn't. And now, no doubt, she would soon be cooked up for supper, for of course the farther he walked, the hungrier he would be getting, just ready for a nice little bit of white meat like herself.

She whimpered forlornly, and hoped he was not going to be Too Perfectly Horrible. But the only thing to do was to trudge right on in the track of Friday's footprints, for already in her own mind she was calling him "Friday," partly because the day was actually Friday, but mostly because the famous Mr. R. Crusoe-of-the-story-book named his footprint friend Friday.

Then suddenly around a bend in the winding

trail she saw him squatting right in the middle of the path, eating something that was partly wrapped in a big green leaf.

Miss Robinson Crusoe wondered what you ought to do on meeting your man Friday. Naturally she wanted most of all to dash back to the place where mother was, but before she had time to turn around his quick ear had heard her footfall, and he sprang up with his spear poised ready to dart at the unseen enemy. But when he saw the comical little white thing he stood stock-still, exactly as if he had been turned into a big brown statue.

"I w-wish h-he w-was in a m-m-museum!" Miss Crusoe stuttered to herself, as she stood petrified with fear, suddenly remembering how awfully nice it had been to be alive all these years, the daughter of that most adorable mumsy, the pet of all those lovely missionaries. All her own fault . . . never would she disobey again . . . but of course there never would be an "again," this was the end.

As for Friday himself, he could hardly believe his eyes. Decidedly, she must be a sort of goblin, for her face was white like fleecy little clouds, tinted pink at sunset time. And her eyes were blue like twin lakes in the sunshine; her hair was tawny like a lion's mane, and she was decorated round and round, in the queerest get-up he had ever seen on anyone. The more he looked the surer he was that she was a spirit, so he lowered his spear and knelt down very reverently; having nothing else to offer, he held out his banana-leaf meal.

"O joy!" gasped little Miss Robinson Crusoe, inside, "he's going to be friends instead of having me for lunch," so she nibbled very daintily at the plantain paste and took a peanut or two, while he grunted with surprise and pleasure.

Then she said a sentence to him in the black man's language which her mother had taught her. And he said a sentence to her. But her sentence and his sentence were not in the same language, for he belonged to a tribe far off from the place where they now were. All of which made it hard to be friends successfully, since they had to talk with their fingers. But she could see in his eyes the most pleasant kind of worship, as if he thought she might disappear into thin air any moment. So when she pointed to the path ahead, and beckoned him to come along with her, he nodded and grunted. And off they started, hand in hand.

She was such a very little person, and he was such a very tall one (also, very, very black!) that when he took big long steps she had to hop-skip-and jump to keep up with him, until finally they came walking together into town.

A certain Mrs. Missionary, on her veranda, looked up in surprise. "Henry," she called to her husband indoors, "who ever is this giant whom little Robin has in tow? I don't see how her mother dares let her out alone on these forest trails. See, I'm sure he's a perfect stranger."

"He is!" Miss Robinson Crusoe sang out proudly, "for I discovered him all by myself from his footprints, when I was being a Babe-in-the-woods by mistake. I call him Friday, and he never even tried to gobble me up. Maybe Uncle Henry can palaver with him, for he doesn't talk words that I know."

So on that memorable Friday evening, by torch-light, Mr. Missionary, who knew many languages,

palavered a long while with the man Friday. It
seemed that he belonged in a kraal way back in the
forest where-the-sun-goes-down. One day the chief
of his village died, and the witch-doctor fastened
all the blame on him. The furious villagers tried to
get him to take poison to prove whether he was
innocent or guilty. But his legs were long and his
lungs were good, so he took to his heels and ran!
He ran all night by moonlight, with the swift
runners of the village after him; he ducked and
dodged and hid all day, and then ran the next
night, and the next one too, farther and farther
from the place-where-the-sun-goes-down nearer and
nearer to the place-where-the-sun-comes-up.

Then, horror of horrors, just when he felt safest,
he saw a little white goblin in his path. He gave up
all hope. For never had he seen any one whose
face was not brown like mud in the rainy season or
black like wood that is charred. Yet now it seemed
there was a tribe of this cloud-white people—and
from the kindness of their hearts they were doing
their best to make him feel like one of themselves.

He built himself a little hut of palm leaves and
straw and mud, and at first, for a fetish of good luck,
he hung over the door the big banana leaf he had
had out on the forest trail when the dear little white
goblin had caught him.

But as he learned the new language, and watched
the other black people in this village wearing decent
clothes, going to school, and doing things the white
man's way, Friday decided to live their way too,
so he took down the foolish charm. From that day
on Mr. Missionary taught him, and Mrs. Missionary
taught him. Even Miss Robinson Crusoe taught

him. All those nice friendly little things that a Christian child is born knowing, but which a heathen man must hear, hour after hour, to dare believe.

But finally old fears, old superstitions, old prejudices died away, and Friday became a teacher himself. Because his feet were so big and his body so tireless he used to travel all up and down the forest trails to tell the black people the astonishing news of the Lord Jesus. Everybody got to know him, and little black children would scamper into their kraals screaming: "News! News! Friday is here!"

(For when he had to learn a new language, he decided to take a new name too, and Miss Robinson Crusoe simply insisted on its being "Friday." So it was, of course.)

Every minute of every day found him telling the new-old story of the Lord Jesus to somebody somewhere, until you could have discovered the footprints for miles and miles in all directions.

Then one rainy season Friday came down with chills and fever, far from home; and the frightened black people in that kraal did not know what to do for him. They called their witch doctor, who obligingly worked himself up into a fury as he danced around Friday, trying to "smell out" who had made him sick.

But the few new Christians knew this old way was foolishness, so they started to carry him back through the forest to his home. In every kraal through which they went black families watched him passing by, and shaking their dear black heads, they said mournfully, "He is sick with too bad a sickness."

Friday died back in the new village where he had been so happy and little Miss Robinson Crusoe cried as if her poor little heart would break. "I thought my Friday would go on making footprints forever and ever," she sobbed.

"I know, dear," her mother sighed.

And yet this is really not a sad story at all, for something very wonderful happened when the black people back in the forest heard that Friday had gone home to Jesus. They came quietly to town, and one of them said, "Friday told me all that ever I heard of the Lord Jesus. Now that he lives in the town of God, I will give two days each new moon to walk in Friday's footsteps."

A very, very old woman said happily: "I am shown a new thing. I do not know how much, but at least I can carry to my neighbors the good news that Friday brought to me."

"And I will give from the time-when-the-sun-is-in-the-middle-of-the-sky to the time-when-the-sun-goes-down to carrying on Friday's work every day," a young chief said. Others promised an hour a day, or one day a week, or one week in every month— until there were dozens of "Fridays" to go through the black forest like lights in a dark place.

Even to-day, whenever our grown-up Miss Robinson Crusoe goes walking on the jungle trails, and meets any Christian far from home, she hardly needs to ask, "What brings you so far from your own kraal, friend?" for the answer almost always is, "O, this is my day for carrying on Friday's work, teacher."

But no one has ever been known to fear these new footprints of Friday, for it is just as if the Lord Jesus had made them himself right into the hearts and the homes of a people hungry for God.

Friday's Footprints, MARGARET T. APPLEGARTH, pages 1-9, The Judson Press, Philadelphia, Pa. Used by permission of the publisher.

XVIII

PRIVATE TOM MAKES A DISCOVERY

PRIVATE THOMAS COOPER was coming home from
the Great War the long way round. For toward the
last his company had been stationed in Siberia and
they were all being sent back from there by way
of China.

Private Tom was something of a hero, although
you would never know it from anything he said;
but inside his khaki greatcoat was a medal that
had been pinned on him for bravery, and his
shattered arm was still in a sling. So by special
permission, on the plea of ill health, they let him
stop off to rest in a certain Chinese town where for
a special reason Private Tom was delighted to be
dropped. For another hero lived in that town—a
football hero gone to seed.

"Just wait till I wake him up though, the old
stick-in-the-mud!" grinned Private Tom as he ate
breakfast that morning; after which he sallied down
the Chinese street holding his nose with his one good
hand so as not to smell the horrible odors that rose
from the open sewers.

"Imagine choosing a pigsty like this to live in
out of all the places on earth," sniffed Private Tom
in utter disgust, as he strode along through the unspeakable mud of the unspeakable street, which
had a charming name, had he only known it—"The
Street of Ten Thousand Moonbeams." But Private
Tom only wished for his Aunt Arabella's smelling

salts, and was glad when he saw the hospital for which he was bound.

A neat little Blue Cotton Nurse bobbed politely before him as she let him in the door when he asked her for his old college chum.

"I please you to honorably sit," she suggested politely, bowing again.

So he honorably sat, but discovered he was not sitting alone. The maimed and the halt and the blind all touched elbows with him in that waiting room, and although he was a hero he found himself edging away and squeezing himself into as small a space as possible.

Because—O well, just because! Somehow they did not look inviting, those patients, and he hoped the football hero would hurry out to greet him.

He did too!

"Why, Tom, old pal! Who ever expected to have you drop down here! Where'd you come from anyhow?"

"War!" said Private Tom, gripping the hand of the ex-football hero. "Don't suppose you know there's been a war going on for years, though, you old stick-in-the-mud! Say, Dick, what ever made you choose this hole to live in? Never saw such a filthy spot or smelled such smells. Come on out in the country somewhere and let's have a good old pow-wow."

"Sorry, Tom, but you see my patients waiting, and there'll be more in a minute. This is our morning for men; most of them work and must get back to their jobs soon. We'll have to wait until office hours are over at noon. Let me see, what shall I do with you meanwhile?"

"Anything, old man, except keep me cooped in here with the lame and the halt and the blind," shuddered Private Tom. "You make me wild," he blazed; "aren't you a crackerjack doctor? Then why do you stick yourself off among a lot of repulsive Chinks like these?"

"Chinks?" snapped the doctor; "don't you dare call them Chinks! Why, good gracious, Tom, they're the salt of the earth! I've got a fellow in my office this minute who dug trenches behind the lines in France for two years, and his family—O well, if you're so blind; I tell you what I'll do—I'll turn you loose in the hospital in charge of Chow Wan. She speaks a delicious brand of English, and you can spend a ripping morning. Then we'll lunch together. I'll send her in at once. So long!" and he hurried away.

Private Tom sniffed in disgust. Then the Blue Cotton Nurse padded in softly, and beamed at him.

"Honorable doctor say you please I should show you the all things. Honorably sit."

"See here," said Private Tom, shaking a finger at her, "I don't please to sit! Show me something interesting—anything but this roomful of—of—of."

The Blue Cotton Nurse squinted up at him sidewise. "O, but I pleases you to honorably sit just a miserable moment—for there are nothings of more interesting than this what-you-call roomful."

So Private Tom unwillingly sat down on the edge of the bench, with the Blue Cotton Nurse beside him.

"They is all lovely cases," she began, waving her hand to include everybody present. "They is to be like magic in this town. Now that ragged man by

the door; he are chair coolie for big mandarin.
Mandarin are got no use for Christian church; no,
no! But presently chair coolie get sick. He try
quack doctor; no good at all; just more pain, more
trouble. So Mandarin he do send coolie here and
God pleases for Christian pills should make him
healthy. Mandarin smile, and presently are sick
himself and now sends coolie for pills. So God will
to cure him, then he maybe go walk into church
some day—yes?"

Private Tom stared at the chair coolie. Not such
an impossible specimen after all, tattered and tired,
of course, but what a good face!

"Is he a Christian—the coolie, I mean?"

"Half-way," nodded the Blue Cotton Nurse, "he
do get some doubts yet about evil spirits and idols.
But his small girls is in our school now, and when
they comes home singing Jesus songs and telling
Jesus stories, can he be heathen for always?"

Private Tom thought not.

"Now as for man next by the coolie, he are most
dreadful fiend."

"Really?" asked Private Tom. "He just looks
tame and stupid to me."

"O, he are; that are just the matter," exclaimed
the little nurse, "for he are most dreadful opium
fiend; he do sell his baby girl last year for trifling
cash to buy opium. He do never fill the family
rice-bowl, so alas! they die—because he is no work.
Now he got no'inner person left for cooking—no
son, no rooftree—all sold. He got only lonesome
inside him, so now Honorable Doctor took a hand
over him."

Private Tom looked kindly at the dull, heavy

eyes and the sad yellow face. "But can he be helped," he asked.

"O, God are wonderful!" breathed the little nurse. "God do give him strength for not smoke opium since nine weeks. God and Honorable Doctor, can they not make wonders? The man next by, he do get infected eye. Last month it is so big as your fist, all full poison matter; ugh! Where are that big sore now. Gone! Honorable Doctor have cut away."

And so she went on around the roomful, until Private Tom knew about each of them; the particular sickness, the likely cure, the home life, the way they regarded Christianity, until somehow they no longer seemed like just repulsive people to him.

"You love them, don't you?" he asked the Blue Cotton Nurse, as they were shutting the door, about to leave the room.

"But yes!" she said, poking her head inside for a last look. "I please you to remember I were miserable the same way, only worse! Much worser— of so full of unpleasantness. Then God do make me over specially for loving the sick."

Private Tom choked. Good gracious! What a blind fool he had been! He stumbled down the hallway after her into a cheerful, sunny room.

"Childrens!" beamed the little nurse, pointing proudly to the rows of tiny cots, "there are nothings nicer than little Chinese childrens, say our Honorable Doctor. And for every childrens here, there are a mother, and in every mother there are love that Christian hospital do sit in her town for curing her childrens."

Next there was the women's ward, then the men's

ward, then the convalescent ward—all full of
patients, so many that Private Tom said curiously,
"Where's the other doctor?"

"Are you make joke on me?" asked the little
nurse. "For there are no more doctor but the one."

Private Tom looked at the neatly scrubbed floors,
the spotless operating room, the spick and span
halls, and the neat little Chinese nurses and he said:
"It's wonderful—wonderful! Let me go back in
the waiting room, though; I know there are a hundred things you ought to be doing."

The Blue Cotton Nurse said demurely, "O, but
that do be a most smelly place for honorable American nose!"

"I can stand it," Private Tom said bluntly,
wedging himself in between a blind boy and a rough
old beggar. An entirely new crowd were in the
waiting room now, each with some terrible ailment,
some strange history behind him, some unknown
future before him waiting—waiting for the touch of
the Foreign Doctor to cure and to help.

Private Tom looked at the blind boy and thought:
"We were almost twins, little fellow, you and I, but
your doctor opened my eyes in one treatment. I
hope he'll do as well for you. Talk about heroes—
this is a factory where they make them, and I called
him a stick-in-the-mud! Well, now I see!"

So after luncheon Private Tom said enthusi-
astically: "I tell you what, Dick, when I get home
I'm going to boost foreign missions until something
happens. I'm going to tell the fellows it's the place
for real live men to come if they want to be heroes!"

"O, not that!" interrupted the doctor, "there's
no hero job here."

Private Tom took his hand. "Dick," he said, "if I had all the decorations of the European war I'd pin them all on your coat lapel, and kiss you on both cheeks too, as Foch does; for you're a soldier, man; a real live soldier! And this hospital is a real live battle field; every day you have to fight this whole town single-handed, and how you do win out, Dick! How you do win out! Curing the sick, cleaning things up, training your own nurses, doing ten men's work, and keeping bright—and alone! I don't see how you stand it!"

Dick said quietly: "Why, Tom, if I did it alone, I couldn't stand it. But I've got a wonderful Ally; day by day he walks through the wards of this little hospital, he stands beside every cot, he strengthens every nurse, he does the very things I couldn't do, alone."

Private Tom said earnestly: "Dick, even if I never come back as a doctor, as I'd like to do, remember that I'm going to boost. We've been far too quiet about foreign missions back in America, too quiet and too lazy and too ready to leave it to the other fellow. But you can count on me from now on, old pal."

And down in his heart, Private Tom wonders whether you wouldn't like to be a "pal" too? Someone whose eyes have been opened so that you can always be counted on—to boost, and to give, and to pray?

Friday's Footprints, MARGARET T. APPLEGARTH, pages 193-202. The Judson Press, Philadelphia. Used by permission of the publishers, The Judson Press.

XIX

UP NORTH

"That will do, Lincoln. You may sit down," said the teacher.

Lincoln was conscious as he finished reading, that a subdued titter ran around the room. That was the way these strange Northern boys and girls had laughed every time he opened his mouth. Now they laughed softly and secretly, since the teacher had sternly checked them. He knew they were making fun of him because of his Southern accent, and even the eight or ten other Negro boys and girls in the room joined them. He bit his lips to keep the tears back. What was the good of his beautiful, beautiful shining desk all by himself, of the lovely warmth which came from no hot iron stove, but yet seemed to fill the whole room; of the beautiful pictures on the wall; of the real blackboard, if there was no friendly face except that of the teacher?

He looked shyly up at the teacher. She was a white woman, the first white teacher he had ever had; and this was a school for white boys as well as black. There were no schools like that in the South.

Many of the boys, too, were different from any white boys Lincoln had ever seen before. Donald Bliss, a colored boy, had whispered to him at recess that the fathers of Dominico and Tony were Italians, that Stephane's father was a Greek, and that big John was the son of a Bohemian.

The teacher was speaking again. "Will Lincoln

Hall please remain for a few minutes after school?"

In the quiet room Lincoln looked up timidly into the face of his teacher.

"Lincoln," began the teacher, "I think this grade is a little too hard for you yet."

"But I was in the fifth grade at home, ma'am," answered Lincoln, the tears beginning to come into his big black eyes. Was he to be banished from this beautiful room after all?

"Still, your school never lasted so long as our school does, Lincoln, and you had other handicaps, too. Well," she concluded slowly, "I'll try you for a few days. A boy with your name, you know, ought to be able to accomplish anything. You remember Lincoln had to work very hard for his education when he was a boy."

"But—but he was a white boy," answered Lincoln shyly.

"Black boys have done as much," she replied.

Had they, indeed! Lincoln walked proudly to the door. He would just show teacher and all of them that he could stick in that class!

Out on the playground the boys of the fifth grade were building a huge snow fort, which they had topped with a flag. Black boys and white were working together. Would they let him play with them? Big John was just hoisting up a huge block of snow to the top of the fort. "Here, Coon," he called over his shoulder to Lincoln, "you can make the ammunition!"

In spite of the unpleasant name, Lincoln smiled as he walked over to the fort and began making snowballs with his bare hands.

"I'm going to be captain of the fort," exclaimed Dominico, dancing up and down.

"No, me," answered big John roughly. "I guess I built it!"

"But I made de plans and helped," answered Dominico hotly.

"Well, you ain't goin' to be captain," replied John.

"All right, then see what will happen to yer old fort," and reaching behind Lincoln, Dominico gave a push which sent John's newly balanced tower and Lincoln together tumbling to the ground.

John turned upon him in a rage. "You knock down my fort!" he exclaimed, doubling up his fists.

"Naw, he did it," laughed Dominico, pointing to Lincoln, rising from the snow.

"Let's wash his face!" exclaimed Tony.

"I'll show him!" yelled John.

But Lincoln was frightened. He had never been in a snow fight before, and he flung out wildly with his arms, striking as hard as he could, for he was sure he was going to be smothered.

Good-natured Donald Bliss, standing behind him, at this moment heaved a soft block of snow from the fort upon the necks of the boys who were doing the washing.

"Aw, quit!" exclaimed John, fishing down his back.

"Let's run the coons off!" called a white boy.

The cry was taken up. "Let's have a snow fight."

In a second the colored boys found themselves alone, while the white boys were pelting them with snowballs.

And then the battle began in earnest. The Negro boys were far outnumbered. They fought pluckily, but inch by inch they were driven out of the playground and along the street. A well-aimed ball from Donald Bliss knocked John's cap off. Angrily the big boy picked up a hunk of ice and threw it with all his might at Donald. He ducked, but it struck Lincoln full on the cheek bone, and, stumbling sideways, he fell, the blood trickling from a wide gash in his cheek.

"Aw, cut it out!" exclaimed Dominico, running toward Lincoln. "He didn't knock yer fort down anyway. I did," and the Italian boy faced the other white boys defiantly.

"I should think," said a clear voice, "that since both sides fight so pluckily, you could *together* win any sort of battle."

"Miss Oliver!" gasped Donald Bliss.

"And now," continued Miss Oliver, "I think the first thing is to get this cut dressed."

The boys hung their heads in silence.

"Will you come with me?" smiled the lady as she bent over Lincoln.

The boy looked up in her face with round eyes.

"Are—are you a police lady, missis?" he questioned.

The woman shook her head and smiled at him. "I am just a friend of boys," she answered, as she helped him to his feet.

In a few minutes Lincoln found himself in a big, warm building. He looked about him with wide eyes. In a long, sunny room numbers of little Negro boys and girls were playing a merry kindergarten game. In another room tables were being laid with food for them. In a third room some big colored boys were laughing over a game of dominoes. From somewhere upstairs came the sound of music on a piano. "Please, ma'am," asked Lincoln, "where is this?"

"It is just a big, friendly church home kept by the Mission Board for all the colored people of this neighborhood," answered the lady.

"I think it's heaven!" answered Lincoln with a sigh of comfort.

In a neat little office, while the lady dressed his cut, Lincoln poured out the whole story; how his father had been sick with a bad cough this winter and had to stay home from work many days; how they lived on the top floor of a rickety old building so close to the elevated railroad that the cars seemed to thunder through their rooms night and day; how sister Caroline wanted to go back home down South where the morning glories grew in the summer over their little cottage and the hollyhocks and sunflowers stood in the garden; and little lame Georgie was afraid of the dashing automobiles and cars, and cried all the time with the cold; how Mammy knew no families to wash for in this strange city; and, last of all, about the old blue tin box and the two silver dollars in it.

"But ef I has to spend the money fo' grub, then I can't go to college ever," he concluded sadly.

"O, I guess you won't have to do that," comforted the lady. "I think we can help you out. Just come over to this next office with me. Mrs. Trowbridge," she asked of the lady at the desk, "have you anyone who wants washing done?"

Mrs. Trowbridge glanced down her page.

"Certainly," she replied, "here are several families on my list."

"Anything for a boy?" continued Miss Oliver.

Mrs. Trowbridge considered. And then she nodded. "Yes," she answered. "Old Mrs. Hedges wants a boy to run errands every Saturday afternoon. She will pay fifty cents."

"How will that do, Lincoln?" questioned Miss Oliver.

Lincoln's eyes sparkled. "Maybe some time," he replied, "I put another dollar in that box!"

"Shouldn't wonder," smiled Miss Oliver. "And now, Lincoln, tell your mother I will call on her to-morrow morning about the washing, and I think I know the right doctor for your father to see."

"Please, ma'am," said Lincoln, twisting his hat in his hands, "you've been so powerful good, could Georgie come here sometimes and listen to the music? He surely kin play on the ol' fiddle."

"Certainly he may come, and sister too. Perhaps she would like to join some of our classes for young girls."

Still Lincoln lingered. "Miss Oliver," he stammered, "did—did you say you belong to a Mission Board?"

Miss Oliver nodded, smiling.

"There was a Mission Board friend down South, too. I—I got *two* frien's now," said Lincoln shyly.

"I hope you will have many more," answered Miss Oliver, as she opened the door for him.

But Lincoln stood still in astonishment. There, in a silent line, were the boys of his school, colored and white together. What had happened to them? One of Donald Bliss' eyes was swollen shut. Tony

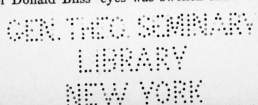

had lost his hat. Dominico's lip was bleeding, but big Bohemian John carried in triumph a small, torn American flag. What did it all mean?

"Why, boys!" exclaimed Miss Oliver, looking at them over Lincoln's head, "have you been fighting ever since I left you?"

"Yeh-er," replied big John, a grin spreading over his scratched face. "Dose bad boys from de Green Street school dey come to take de flag from our fort. We fight—we fight *togedder*, an' we keep de flag!

"Yeh-er, we kept it!" broke in Donald.

"And now we make a parade wit de flag," declared John. "An'—an' we stop here for Lin."

"Come on, Lin!" called Dominico, grabbing Lincoln by the arm. "We mak-a da friends, me an' you!" and with a yell the boys were off, the flag waving proudly in the lead.

From *The Magic Book*, by ANITA B. FERRIS. Used by permission of the publishers, Council of Women for Home Missions and the Missionary Education Movement of the United States and Canada.

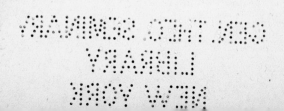